# PACKAGE
# AND PRINT

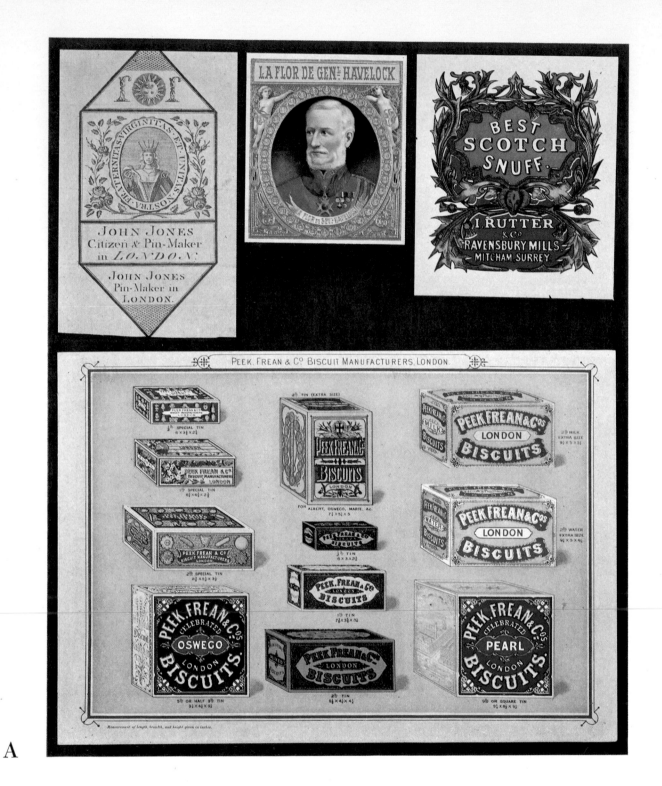

A

Pin-paper *c.* 1730 – a copperplate engraving printed in 'sanguine' red
Cigar-box label and snuff wrapper, both printed in gold and colours; probably late nineteenth century
Group of paper-labelled biscuit tins illustrated in a trade catalogue issued by Peek, Frean & Co,
Bermondsey, shortly before this firm became a limited company (1901)

# ALEC DAVIS

# PACKAGE AND PRINT

# The Development of Container and Label Design

*Clarkson N. Potter, Inc./Publisher* NEW YORK

# FOREWORD

This book would not have been possible without the great help I have had from many friends and correspondents, notably –

the people, firms and organizations named in pages 11–17;

all the other people, firms and organizations who should have been named there but are, by oversight, omitted;

my wife, for unfailing patience during my researches and active help at the proof stages;

Janet Gardner and Stephen Davis for help in typing and in indexing;

Berthold Wolpe for care beyond the line of duty in seeing the book to, and through the press.

A.D.

# CONTENTS

# ILLUSTRATIONS

The location of items in museums or other public collections is given in parentheses.

The illustrations come from the firms whose names appear in them, or from sources named in italics *below*, or (the majority) from the author's collection of packaging photographs.

## COLOUR PLATES

## PLATES

11

# ILLUSTRATIONS

# ILLUSTRATIONS

# ILLUSTRATIONS

# ILLUSTRATIONS

# ILLUSTRATIONS

# ILLUSTRATIONS IN THE TEXT

# ILLUSTRATIONS

# INTRODUCTION

THIS IS A BOOK about packaging before the word 'packaging' was invented – and because the word still means different things to different people, we must start with a definition. 'Packaging' in these pages is a collective term for all the kinds of containers in which goods are packed for sale to the consumer or user. This definition excludes containers mainly intended for transit or for storage, such as crates and sacks, but it includes a whole cavalcade of boxes and bottles, bags and wrappers and 'jarrs with bungs' stretching back further than one might think, to days when branded goods in the modern sense were still unheard of.

From the beginning, most packages have been throwaway things, and early examples are hard to find – especially complete examples in three dimensions: wrappers and flat box-tops and labels have survived more easily, if accidentally, in files of correspondence or between the pages of books (there are now collectors of matchbox labels, beer-bottle labels, and cheese labels). Nowhere is there a large museum of packaging to which the historian can turn, though there are *some* packages in many museums – as the acknowledgments on pages 11 to 17 show.

Descriptions of early packaging are as rare as examples. Samuel Pepys and Daniel Defoe and other close observers of everyday life mention a box or a pot but do not go into details. Nor do the advertisers help us much till we come to the second half of the nineteenth century.

This book is an outline of the development of packaging up to 1914 – the year in which an era ended. It is not an account of modern packaging: of these there have been many already. Nor is it a history of printing: of those there have been even more. It is an attempt to gather together the scanty facts about early packaging before they become even scantier; on the framework of facts the reader may build what edifices he desires – by deduction or guesswork. It will at least be informed guesswork.

Because packaging was not until recently a conscious coherent group of industries, old trade divisions have been followed in some chapters of this book; if it seems a small-minded attitude to discuss, say, tins and cardboard boxes and pots as separate and unrelated things, that is how their makers saw them in the times with which we are concerned.

19

# Social History
# of
# Packaging

An early instance of mechanized packaging – measuring out 12,000
packets of cocoa-essence a day at Cadbury's works in Birmingham.
Illustration from a magazine advertisement of the 1880s

Pins were among the first paper-packaged wares. They were stuck into sheets of paper and then enclosed in the outer wrapper which usually bore the design. Comparison of this pin paper for Nicholls with the earlier example for John Jones, top left in plate A, suggests that the method of folding dictated a uniform shape – the rectangular panel became the front of the packet when it was made-up, and the triangles folded over for the ends. Size $9\frac{1}{4} \times 4\frac{3}{8}$ in.

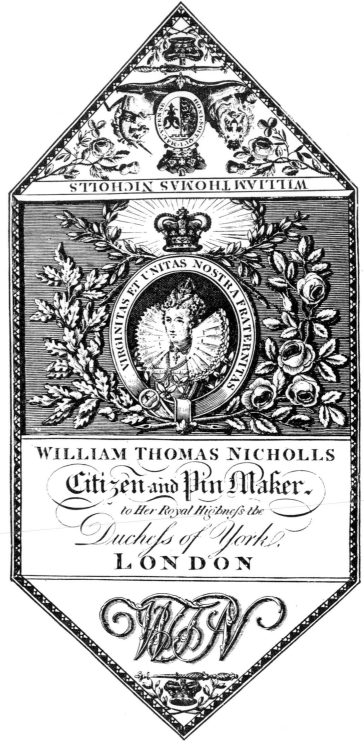

# SOCIAL HISTORY

PACKAGES of one sort and another have played a part in Western man's way of living for longer than most people realize. Though the development of packaging has been largely the result of technical progress, its effects have spread far beyond the technicians, to all of us and our ancestors for generations back. This is a story of everyday things in relation to everyday people – shoppers and 'chymists' and country grocers as well as package-manufacturers and the artists who put the first pictures on packages.

To start the story even further back, the *pre-history* of packaging begins with containers and wrappers of the most elementary kinds – objects which were provided by nature and were only accidentally suitable for the purpose to which man put them. As soon as our ancestors had any valued possessions, they must have needed vessels to hold them and wrapping materials to protect them. Men made use of gourds and hollow tree-trunks long before they had learned to make jars or boxes; animal bladders and skins were the far forerunners of Cellophane; leaves, of wrapping paper. In some African and Eastern markets, leaves are still used in this way today.

## c. 1550-1700

THE REPLACEMENT of natural containers by commercial packages has been an age-long process. To see the beginnings of packaging in the modern sense, we must turn our attention from primitive man to sixteenth-century European man: the conditions that had to be fulfilled before packaging of any kind could flourish were the existence of a trading community, the ability to make containers, the ability to mark them with traders' names, and the ability (among some buyers, if not all) to identify those names. In our civilization these conditions were probably fulfilled for the first time in the paper trade in Germany. German papermakers traded widely; their containers were wrappers which they made as a by-product of their own merchandise, fine paper; they decorated these wrappers with printed designs; and their customers, because they were people who bought paper to write or print on, were bound to be literate. Though I have written of papermakers in the plural, only one papermaker's wrapper of the period (plate 45) is known to exist today: we must acknowledge Andreas Bernhart, at his paper mill on the Ocker in the 1550s, as the earliest recorded practitioner of packaging. . . at a time when Queen Elizabeth was scarcely on the throne of England, William Shakespeare was yet unborn and North America was still the Indians'.

The dates when anybody did anything for the first time in the history of packaging can only be estimated from the few packages and the few fragments of information which have come down to us. There were no contemporary trade papers to record such minutiae as Mr X's first use of tobacco wrappers or Mr Y's handsome new pin papers, and, understandably, the general trend towards more packaging did not qualify as news in the slim newspapers of the time, which were fully occupied with wars, crimes and natural disasters. However, it is from the advertisement columns of the early London newspapers that we learn of vendors of quack medicines who were, by the 1660s, packaging their wares in paper wrappers marked with their signatures, written or printed, and with coats of arms known or unknown to any college of heralds. So much we learn from the advertisements, but no direct evidence in the form of actual paper packages of the period is known to exist. There may be an additional reason for this besides the passage of time: the Great Fire of London, whose effects are discussed in more detail on page 50.

The only example of English packaging from the years before the fire is an innkeeper's wine-bottle found at Wellingborough, Northants, dated 1657 (plate 25). By 1669, at least one London tobacconist was using printed wrappers; this earliest example of English paper packages is Thomas Lacy's (plate 47: see also page 50). The general scarcity of packaging in the seventeenth century is, however, more accurately reflected in an advertisement in a London newspaper of 1680, which warns the prospective purchaser of tea to 'bring a convenient Box'.

# Eighteenth century

WE ARE INCLINED to think of the eighteenth century in England (and in Europe generally) as an age of elegance, of taste, of wit, but not of trade: the century of Bath, not Birmingham. But it was a time of commercial expansion on a scale the world had never seen before. The schism between intellectual and industrialist which was later to bedevil English society was not yet wide, if it existed at all. James Thomson wrote approvingly of his England, the England of 1730:

> Then Commerce brought into the public Walk
> The busy Merchant; the big Warehouse built;
> Rais'd the strong Crane; choak'd up the loaded Street
> With foreign plenty.

John Dyer, in 1757, heard

> th'echoing hills repeat
> The stroke of axe and hammer,

and saw 'the redd'ning fields' of Manchester, Sheffield, and Birmingham 'rise and enlarge their suburbs'.

Later, the epitaph on Josiah Wedgwood (1730–1795) recorded the fact that he had 'converted a rude and inconsiderable manufactory into an elegant Art and an important part of the National Commerce'. There is no hint that the two phrases on either side of the 'and' would, a generation or two later, be regarded as conflicting or even contradictory. This was a century in which Hogarth could, without condescension, design trade cards; and Baskerville could make a fortune from japanned ware in Birmingham while designing a type-face that would bring him international renown.

One must admit that there is no evidence of talents such as these applied to package design – nor of any spectacular growth of packaging. An early eighteenth-century London grocer's stock list[1] includes seventy items in alphabetical order from almonds to vermicelli, but it does not

---

[1] Lancelot Sharpe's, of Fenchurch Street, *c.* 1717; reproduced in *A History of Shopping* by Dorothy Davis.

mention a single manufacturer's name or brand-name, and includes only one reference to a packed commodity: 'Bottled Fruits for Tarts'. A few names seen on packages today were, however, 'in' before the eighteenth century was out – among them Burgess, Keiller, Lazenby, Twining, Yardley, and Singleton (whose eye ointment was already old-established). Bottled beers were on the market – and so were bottled antidotes for too much beer; there were pots of snuff, prepared mustard, and a variety of ointments; there were paper 'pacquets' for such diverse contents as tea and sago powder, pins and tobacco. Eighteenth-century tobacco papers provide one of the first opportunities for international comparisons in packaging: between English and Dutch and later Norwegian wrappers.

AMERICA, up to the time of achieving her independence in 1776, had not even begun to feel the strength in her industrial sinews but imported most of her manufactured luxuries, and some virtual necessities of a developing civilization, from Europe. There is no first-hand evidence of packaging in Colonial days, but it is evident that trade in consumer goods was developing. By the 1720s the American Colonies had newspapers which devoted half their space to advertisements and shipping notices. By the 1740s, the chain of activities which began with wholesale merchants at the ports was continued by retail shopkeepers and 'a motley crew of hawkers and pedlars, who carried wares from foreign parts into the the household itself'.[1] Some of these were probably packaged wares from England or France, Holland or Germany.

It would however be misleading to think that because packages were being made in the eighteenth century, the world that used them was our world. *We* were far fewer: nine million in Britain in 1794; in America, one million in 1750, seven million in 1810. Moreover there was little inducement for any but the most urbane traders to print names and addresses or directions for use on their packs while most of the population could not read: only 80,000 were literate in Britain's nine million, and it is doubtful whether the proportion in other countries was significantly higher.[2]

If the demand for packaging was minute by the standards of later centuries, the supply was microscopic. Up to the end of the eighteenth century, every label or wrapper was printed by hand with wooden presses on hand-made paper; every bottle, too, was hand-made. It is remarkable that packaging of any kind had gained a foothold in these conditions: but surviving examples show that it had.

# Nineteenth century

THE PATH of history does not usually turn a corner or cross a bridge at the end of one century and the beginning of another: but it so happens that in the history of packaging three notable innovations came almost simultaneously and almost at the end of the eighteenth century. They

---

[1] OSCAR HANDLIN: *The American people: a new history* (1963).

[2] A question about literacy was included in the United States census in 1840, but there are no reliable figures before 1870, when illiterates were 20 per cent of the total population.

were the invention of a papermaking machine; the discovery of lithography; and the beginnings of American packaging.

To take the last item first: the oldest American pack known to exist today is a label or wrapper for paper made at the Luke Bemis mill at Watertown, Massachusetts (1799–1805). It was printed from a simple wood-block with the arms of Massachusetts.

The papermaking machine was invented in France in 1798 by Nicolas-Louis Robert, a bookkeeper at Leger Didot's paper mill. Because of the unsettled state of France at that time, so soon after the Revolution, his invention was developed in England by Bryan Donkin, with the backing of two London stationers and papermakers, the Fourdrinier brothers. A logical sequel to the invention of paper machines was John Dickinson's invention, some years later, of the first machine to make *board*, at his mill in Hertfordshire; and soon afterwards (in 1831) the first American machine-made strawboard was produced by George A. Shryock of Chambersburg, Pennsylvania.

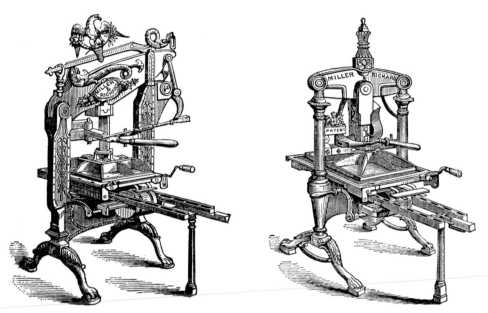

From hand-powered wooden presses, the next step forward in printing was to presses which were still hand-powered but iron-framed. The Columbian, by George Clymer, was introduced in the USA in 1813 and later made in Britain as well; the Albion, by Richard Whittaker Cope of London, appeared *c.* 1822

The principle of lithography was discovered by Alois Senefelder in Bavaria in 1798. This new method of printing was later to prove especially suitable for the reproduction of multi-coloured designs in large quantities; in London there were 700 lithographers by 1854, and in the United States the number rose from under thirty at the mid-century to 700 in 1887. It was inevitable, at this time when cardboard boxes and tins as well as bottles and wooden boxes were paper-labelled, that many lithographers should print labels. The names in the first American *Lithographers' Directory* (1887) include Robert Gair, the pioneer of machine-made cartons, and

Geo. S. Harris & Sons, who printed some colourful cigar-box labels (e.g. plate 79). There were many entries under the heading of 'Label Manufacturers', four under 'Labels for Druggists' and ten under 'Labels – Cigar'. The production of lithographed cigar labels was interesting enough to merit a long article in the *New York Sun* in 1888: 'a few years ago any kind of label was considered good enough to put on a cigar box', the *Sun* commented. 'They then cost about $10 for 1,000; the average price paid now is $50. The label is often better than the cigar. . . .'

To LIST all the innovations which accelerated the progress of packaging during the nineteenth century would be an impossible task: some of them are discussed in detail in the following chapters; here their direction can only be broadly indicated. Of the broad trends, these were the most significant:

first and most widespread, the passing of the initiative in packaging from shopkeepers trading locally to manufacturers trading nationally,

second, the packers' need for entirely new kinds of machinery – not only machines to *make* packages but machines to weigh their contents and fill and seal them,

third, the increasingly important part played by America in every aspect of packaging.

The century of Queen Victoria and Abraham Lincoln was also the century of the railways and the first Atlantic steamships. They made the movement of goods over long distances easier than it had been before, and so helped to bring into existence a new phenomenon, the *manufacturer trading nationally* in consumer goods. Ease of movement is, however, a relative term, and in America packages tended to be stronger and larger than in Britain, presumably because of the cross-country joltings of Wells Fargo and the rural housewife's need to lay in a month's – if not a year's – supply of shopping at a time. It is not always possible to tell whether a pack was designed mainly for the country store's use or for its customers' (plates D, 75, 148, 149).

Though railways were a nineteenth-century technical triumph on both sides of the Atlantic, some of the new manufacturers were well on the way to success before the horse-and-carriage days were ended. Several of the longest-lasting consumer-goods businesses in England were launched in towns well away from the capital *before* the railway reached them. The first customers for Joseph Huntley's[1] Reading biscuits were stage-coach passengers; and John Horniman was selling packet tea from the Isle of Wight at a time when the whole of England had only one short railway line. It is not altogether irrelevant to note that when American bottle-makers first pledged 'SUCCESS TO THE RAILROAD' in their designs, they illustrated horse-drawn railroad trucks.

John Horniman's success was due to the conspicuous honesty of his trading methods. He sold tea in sealed packets clearly marked with the price, and this price was based on the net weight of tea alone – not on tea plus paper plus lead foil lining as was common at the time. The first vendors of Horniman's tea were pedlars; chemists and confectioners came next, and grocers last of all; they were reluctant to display the named packets which might outsell their own blends of tea – as, of course, they eventually did.

Horniman was one of the first packers (*c.* 1826) to experience *the need for packaging machinery*; to meet this need he invented an elementary but workable device with which his tea packets

---

[1] His elder son Thomas baked the biscuits and his younger son Joseph made the tins: see pages 71–72.

could be filled accurately and much more quickly than they could have been without it, however skilled the hands of the fillers.

Though labour was still cheap, many other packers were to follow Horniman's lead by introducing labour-saving devices. By the 1880s, Cadbury Bros of Birmingham could, and did, boast of a packing machine that would measure out 12,000 packets of cocoa in a day (page 21); a decade later, the Quaker Oats Company in Ohio was using a machine that weighed out portions of oats and filled cartons with them at the rate of twenty a minute. One does not need to be a mathe-

John Horniman

**Half-pound at 3s 4d 1s. 8d.**
## HORNIMAN'S
## PURE mixed TEA
the BLACK is _not_ artificially colored,
the GREEN is a natural dark olive leaf,
_not_ covered with the usual bluish powder.

"*Tea costs the public annually twelve millions sterling, therefore its purity and reliable quality claims consideration.*"

House of Commons' Report on Tea.

GREAT STRENGTH combined with *fine flavour* is indispensable in tea, to obtain this all know that *young* leaves must alone be infused: *therefore Horniman & Co. import their tea NOT disguised with the usual colouring powder.* The *Times* in a leading article, August 15th, regrets that importers generally, to obtain extra gain, continue to encourage the Chinese to cover with mineral colour an article of daily consumption, so that inferior wintry leaves are made to counterfeit the best tea, and be passed off to the loss of the British consumer.

The extensive demand for Horniman's Tea, proves that the public appreciate its fine flavour, purity and great strength; therefore to enable purchasers to *identify this tea*, it is necessarily sold *only in packets*—never loose—the label is always signed *Horniman&Co* LONDON. 29, 30, 31 & 32, *Wormwood St., City.—Wholesale.*

CHEMISTS, CONFECTIONERS OR BOOKSELLERS are AGENTS in all parts of the kingdom

---

FULL WEIGHT without package.
*Two Ounces at 3s. 4d.* **5d.**
HORNIMAN'S
## PURE mixed TEA,
the GREEN is a natural olive, the BLACK is not artificially coloured.

"*Tea costs the public annually twelve millions sterling, therefore its purity and reliable quality claims consideration.*"
House of Commons Report on Tea.

HORNIMAN & Co's. *imports are NOT disguised with the colouring powder generally used by the Chinese on this article of daily consumption,* to increase their profit, for the artificial colour is employed to make inferior wintry leaves counterfeit the best, and sell as such to the consumers loss.

The extensive demand for Horniman's Tea, proves that the public appreciate its fine flavour, purity and great strength; therefore to enable purchasers to *identify this tea*, it is necessarily sold *only in packets*—never loose—the label is always signed *Horniman&Co* *Wormwood St. City,* LONDON—*Wholesale only*

CHEMISTS OR CONFECTIONERS are Agents in all parts of the kingdom

---

FULL WEIGHT without Package.
*One Ounce at 3s. 4d.* **2½d.**
HORNIMAN'S
*PURE mixed TEA,*
the BLACK not artificially colored, the GREEN a natural dark olive leaf.
*not covered with the usual bluish powder.*

"*Tea costs the public annually twelve millions sterling, therefore its purity and reliable quality claims consideration.*"
House of Commons' Report on Tea.

HORNIMAN & Co.'s *imports are NOT disguised with the colouring powder generally used by the Chinese on this article of daily consumption,* to increase their profit, for the artificial color is employed to make inferior wintry leaves counterfeit the best, and sell as such to the consumers loss.

The extensive demand for Horniman's Tea, proves that the public appreciate its fine flavour, purity and great strength; therefore to enable purchasers to *identify this tea*, it is necessarily sold *only in packets*—never loose—the label is always signed *Horniman&Co* LONDON.
Chemists, Confectioners or Booksellers are Agents in all parts of the Kingdom.

Labels from packets of Horniman's tea, probably about 1870: one of the few instances in packaging of the revived popularity of the Caslon type-face which was evident in English book-typography from the 1840s onwards

matician to see that this was the same speed as at Cadburys', if one can reasonably assume that in each case the working day was ten hours long.

These examples are drawn from the field of paper and cardboard packaging, but for firms whose packs were glass bottles, also, filling and closing were operations that cried out for mechanization. When Whitbreads began beer-bottling in London in 1866, they used the method known as *boot and flogger*; a bottle was placed in a leather 'boot' or 'bucket' which the operator usually held between his knees or strapped to one thigh and the cork was driven home by blows from the 'flogger'. An experienced man could cork 288 dozen bottles a day – an example of the benefits of specialization if not of the dignity of human toil. Later a hand-operated machine increased each man's output; later again, a power machine, driven by gas, did better still.

The third significant nineteenth-century trend, the expansion of *American activity* in every form of packaging, is so evident in every subsequent chapter that it need not be emphasized here. The history of carton-making in America could be adequately recorded at second hand by recording the orders which British boxmakers sent to America for new machinery. The American press-maker Bliss was able to sell machinery for making metal boxes in Britain from about 1875 onwards.

But the flow of packaging materials was not all in one direction. The American canning industry grew up on South Wales tinplate because the United States had no tinplate manufacturing industry of their own until the 1880s. The first carton-makers in England imported much of their boxboard from the U.S.A. and some from France: and it was a Frenchman, Maurice Cartiaux, who made an early attempt, in 1887, to establish a strawboard industry in Britain – at a small factory on the north bank of the Thames at Purfleet (plate 114). His efforts did not prosper for more than a few years, but in 1902 the Thames Paper Co Ltd (later Thames Board Mills Ltd) began operations on the same site – and *this* company was established by an American, William J. Alford.

IN EXPLORING the history of packages, one's researches become inevitably and not unpleasantly involved in the history of their contents. Many of these were products which are unknown to the shopper of today. It is hard to realize that some of them existed at the same time as packaging of even the simplest kind: but it is a fact that Americans used to buy blotting sand in neatly labelled paper packets and Englishmen bought bear's grease (as a hair dressing) in pots with printed lids. During the nineteenth century the protection of the package was also extended to such diverse things as quill pens (plates C and 86), candles (plate 118), wasp-waisted corsets, American paper collars (plates D and 88), Leicestershire hose,[1]

> Vests and pants and shoes with laces,
> And the things you buy in places
> Down in Brompton Road . . .

If packaging was something of a luxury for shoes, it was a necessity for shoe-blacking. . . In the slushy streets of nineteenth-century towns, blacking was no doubt more valuable than it is

---

[1] William Pickering, a Hinckley printer, started to make printed cartridge-paper hose wrappers in 1871.

today, and we know that for most Victorians well-polished boots were essential as a symbol of rectitude (as they still are for guardsmen); but I suspect there must be some subtler explanation, now lost, for the importance of the blacking industry on both sides of the Atlantic. The first reported case in which the infringement of a trademark was restrained by the law of England concerned a blacking label: Day *v* Day, in the Court of Chancery, 1816. From what other product as homely as blacking could a man have made a fortune of £450,000 by 1837, as one of the Days – Charles, of Day & Martin – did? To what other trade could John Propert have turned so successfully that his name would still be considered worth retaining by a large industrial group a century later?

Some blacking was liquid, some paste; some sold in bladders, some in glass jars (plates 41–44), some in pots (plates C and 6), and some in tins (plate 130). The leading makers' names were evidently familiar to the public in 1837: when the reader of *Pickwick Papers* first meets Sam Weller, at the White Hart Inn in High Street, Borough, Sam is polishing boots 'with a polish which would have struck envy to the soul of the amiable Mr Warren, (for they used Day and Martin at the White Hart).' There is a Day & Martin blacking pot, with an elaborate paper label, among the souvenirs of Charles Dickens' life and times in the London house where he once lived, 48 Doughty Street.

OF THOSE products which tempted the shopper's purse a hundred years ago and have survived to tempt it now, many could not have succeeded, and could scarcely have existed, without packaging. Canned food is the classic example – processing and packaging are indivisible in the canning industry; and canned goods could never have achieved their wide popularity if there had not been available a form of package that was light, strong and airtight, and could be made and filled cheaply enough to be discarded after use.

Canning is an obvious instance, but not the only one, of the mutual dependence of nineteenth-century products and packages. Matches would not have sold as they did if there had been no matchboxes – small, cheap containers in which they could be bought; *on* which, moreover, they could be struck. Liquid ink might have taken many years more to supersede ink powder if bottles of glass or stoneware had not been readily available and inexpensive by the second half of the nineteenth century (and Jabez Wilson, in Conan Doyle's *The Red-headed League*, could not have bought his 'penny bottle of ink' to go with his quill pen and seven sheets of foolscap paper).

These products, and many others typical of nineteenth-century industry, were not exotic luxuries appealing to the carriage trade. The new manufacturers were less concerned with the wealthy classes of their own district than with the new market made up from a prosperous urban middle-class and a growing army of artisans who collectively were able to buy vast quantities of reasonably priced goods, ill-paid though they might be individually.

THAT hard work and small pay were not unknown among boxmakers themselves is evident from the life-story of Mrs Cooper, a country craftswoman of the days before boxmaking became an industry, as told by her son, Thomas Cooper, a self-educated lecturer, journalist, and Chartist. As a young widow, in 1810, his mother went from door to door in her native town of Gainsborough, trying to sell pasteboard boxes which she had made: 'But finding little encouragement she began to journey to the surrounding villages and farmhouses, carrying her burden – the smaller boxes within the large, often to the amount of twenty or thirty – on her head.'

In 1811 Mrs Cooper moved into a house in one of the main streets of Gainsborough, where she could display her boxes in a small bow window. But customers had still to be sought; once a week she made the twelve-mile journey by foot and ferry-boat to Epworth market; and she 'had all along hard work to get a decent living, and pay her way'.

To call the industrious Mrs Cooper a package manufacturer would be misleading, for the big boxes she made were intended as trunks to hold servants' clothes, and the smaller ones were sold as workboxes to tradesmen's wives and daughters: she might well have been more prosperous if she *had* been able to work up a trade with consumer-goods manufacturers but clearly there were none on her rural rounds (or none who thought their products would sell better in boxes). She is one of the first people in or near the packaging industries about whom, as a person, anything at all has been recorded.

Another agreeably human figure is the ex-militia colonel, ex-shoemaker of Brunswick, Maine, Andrew Dennison. Colonel Dennison was nudged into the boxmaking business in 1844 by one of his sons, and six years later another son was nudging him to move away from Maine to be nearer the market – for jewellers' boxes – in Boston, Massachusetts. His letter of protest sums up the underlying conflict between two ways of living:

> With respect to my removing my Factory to Roxbury. . . . What could I do for my ample room for all purposes; and for my cow, hens, garden, celler and well and ice house. . . Then again the little farm on the hill where I cut hay for my cow. . . . And then again our convenient church to repair to on Sundays where we can be as comfortable in any weather as we can be in our own houses furnished with a good clock and Bell with other conveniences too numerous to mention . . .

Had Colonel Dennison read Virgil in his schooldays?

We catch another glimpse of the life of a nineteenth-century boxmaker in the story of Andrew Ritchie of Glasgow, who founded his business in 1850 when he was nineteen years old. His wife was two years younger, and they lived in a flat which was both home and workplace. 'The Ritchies hardly ever stopped working. Even on the Sabbath Day, when they came back from the evening service at the kirk, they'd put on the flour paste to boil for the box-making on the morrow. . .'[1]

A slightly more relaxed figure – by the time he was in his fifties at any rate – was Elisha Smith Robinson, paper bag maker and founder of a famous Bristol business. He found time to be an active member of the Baptist church, to stand for parliament twice, and to travel as far afield as India. Yet Robinson never left his 'shop' behind him: from out the depths of the mysterious East came a letter to Bristol describing a paper mill in Delhi which was making 'a very common whitey-brown paper by hand'. This was too much for the opposition newspaper at the time of the next election campaign: it reported a thinly disguised Elisha Smith Robinson asking the multitude in a Buddhist temple, '. . . how can you appreciate all your blessings unless you have

[1] HOUSE: see bibliography.

a large supply of plain and coloured tea-papers, reams of brown wrapping paper and great quantities of paper bags?'

The conceit of Thomas W. Dyott and the impatience of Robert Gair will be evident from subsequent pages: but few of the characters in this book led their private lives in public, and the human interest of the subject resides in the fact that packaging was for people: packaging reflected changing needs and desires and the increasingly urban and industrial way of life of every Western country.

G. M. TREVELYAN wrote that 'many articles that were luxuries in 1837 were common comforts in 1897'; it may be added that many of the common comforts were packaged, advertised, branded goods. Names such as Kodak and Heinz, Nestlé and Suchard, were making themselves known internationally: and the nation which had led the Industrial Revolution was not very far behind in the new art of trumpet-blowing. This phrase is almost literally right for Thomas Lipton, who made his first direct purchase of tea from the growers in 1889, and had fifty dray-loads of it driven through the streets of Glasgow, suitably placarded and accompanied by brass bands and pipers. Horses, elephants, and traction engines dragged his name into the limelight; and Lipton was a millionaire before he was 40.

The pros and cons of advertising have been discussed too often to call for any further discussion here. The growth of pictorial advertising has been a great boon for historians of packaging at any rate: from the late nineteenth century onwards, more and more advertisers illustrated their products in newspaper advertisements, catalogues, showcards, enamelled iron signs, and posters, and from the illustrations (plates 198–208) it is possible to see what packages of the period looked like instead of having to rely on verbal references as we must do for so many earlier packages.

Before most of the advertisers had got round to it, a Victorian artist, James Collinson, had illustrated several packages in one of his *genre* paintings, *At the Bazaar*, 1857. This picture, now in the Graves Collection at Sheffield, shows a variety of 'Useful and Fancy Articles' for a St Bride's Church bazaar including a straw-covered eau de cologne bottle similar to some twentieth-century packs for the 4711 brand; a wooden box of children's building blocks with a label on its sliding lid; an octagonal (metal?) box; and a bear's grease jar which appears to be of glass with a paper label.

# 1900 - 1914

ONE INVENTION at the end of the nineteenth century was of more than technical significance because it encouraged a trend, which was already evident, for package-using firms to produce certain kinds of packaging themselves instead of buying from outside suppliers. Clearly there were practical and economic advantages in being able to start with a reel of plain paper or board, print it in colours, make it up into cartons, and fill them and seal them, all in one's own factory as part of the routine of production. The logical French mind and the trained engineering skill

B

Food packs of 1897 as a colour blockmaker of 1897 saw them. This illustration originally appeared in the *British Printer*, not for the interest of its subject-matter but to demonstrate the then new three-colour halftone process.[1] It was described as 'Reproduced Direct in Three Printings (from) Blocks by John Swain & Son . . . Printed with Mander Brothers' Photochromotype Inks' by Raithby, Lawrence of Leicester – printers of the *British Printer* in 1897 as in 1967

Technically the most advanced of the packs illustrated, the bottle for Heinz's Tomato Chutney (H. J. Heinz Co, Pittsburgh) had a Phoenix metal cap

[1] In this plate, the original three-colour picture (reduced in size from $7\frac{3}{8} \times 6\frac{5}{8}$ in.) is reproduced by the four-colour process which is normal today.

of Louis Chambon made this possible; and the record 39,000,000 visitors to the Universal Exhibition in Paris in 1900 could, if they were so minded, see the 'in-line' printing machine (plate 72) on which Chambon had been working for a decade. This machine made use of a rigid bed or base on which the separate appliances were so rigidly mounted and so precisely driven that colours printed at different stages still printed in register with each other, and the slitting and creasing of carton board could also be effected on the rotary principle. The award of a Grand Prix to Chambon at the 1900 exhibition was the start of a long-continuing success story for his system.

By this time all the staple materials of present-day packaging, with the one exception of plastics, were in regular use –

|       |         |       |
|-------|---------|-------|
| paper | pottery | metal |
| board | glass   | foil  |

– and within the next few years, plastics arrived on the packaging scene inconspicuously, in the form of clear Cellophane film. This material was invented (and given its name) by Dr Jacques Edwin Brandenberger, a Swiss chemist, in 1912, and first manufactured in France in the following year by La Cellophane S.A.

The polishing paste pot in nineteenth-century style was still current in 1926; the carton for a bottle of cod liver oil and malt extract, in 1940

Another new wrapping material of this period was aluminium foil, first made in the United States by the Aluminum Co of America and in Britain by the Empire Aluminium Co, established in Glasgow in 1910. Its arrival on the scene as an alternative to lead and tin foils foreshadowed a problem that was to become increasingly familiar in the twentieth century: for the manufacturers of most consumer goods the difficulty was no longer to find *any* suitable packaging material but to choose the most suitable from a number of alternatives. Commercial revolution had followed the Industrial Revolution, and the box and bag and bottle-makers were carried forward on a rising tide of success. For many the success was to last a long time; a considerable number of firms mentioned in this book are still active today – some under old names and new ownership, a few still guided by the families from which their founders came, generations back.

By 1914, the end of a chapter, packaging had moved out of its old-world phase, the phase of pin papers and pomade pots, into a world of cartons and Crown caps and Tommy Tickler's Jam. The more astute traders, at least, were beginning to realize that a good-looking package could help to *sell* its contents as well as protecting them. The packages in the shops of 1914, though not the same as today's, are recognizably the forerunners of today's; and the historical interest of the subject diminishes after this date. The scope and the sheer volume of packaging, not its character, have changed beyond measure in the last half-century. More and more packaging has given us a litter problem unknown to earlier generations, but it has also given us high standards of hygiene, easier shopping, and just occasionally the kingfisher flash of beauty to surprise the shopper's eye.

# Materials
# of
# Packaging

Round box for plate powder, in use early in the
present century

A 'book' of pins, as illustrated in the 1893 catalogue
of D. F. Tayler & Co, Birmingham

'Stone ginger', i.e. ginger beer in stoneware bottles, was popular enough for printers to want stock blocks of the bottles: those illustrated are from a specimen book of Vizetelly, Branston & Co's designs, issued by Wood & Sharwoods *c.* 1840.

Such bottles could be bought from the Staffordshire Potteries at 10*s* a gross in 1853. Examples which have appeared in bric-à-brac shops recently are perhaps not as old as one might imagine, as they mostly come from rural areas – e.g. the Isle of Wight (Greenham & Co), South Lincolnshire (Lee & Green) – where stone ginger was still bottled in recent years

# (1)
# POTTERY

THE POTTER'S is one of the oldest crafts. There were pots for kohl (eye-shadow) in ancient Egypt, and amphorae for wine in Greece and Rome: the amphorae were sometimes stamped on the handle to indicate the date of manufacture.

Ointment pots and pill pots were made in England from Elizabethan times, but generally they were ornamented only with blue rings or stripes, and they bore no inscription. The Earl of Bedford's household accounts for April 1675 – quoted in Gladys Scott Thomson's *Life in a Noble Household 1641–1700* – contain references to pots which were presumably of this simple kind:

|  |  | s | d |
|---|---|---|---|
| Lidia Long | *A pot of pills* | 2 | 0 |
| Mr Cole's child | *A pot of ointment* | | |
| | *for the stomach* | 1 | 6 |

Half-a-century later, Daniel Defoe – with his journalistic gift for the memorable phrase – recorded that a Windermere delicacy, 'the fish called charrs, . . . came potted to London'.

Pottery 'arrived' as a packaging material with the appearance of traders' names (and sometimes addresses) on small blue-and-white vessels of tin-enamelled earthenware, otherwise known as English delftware. They were of two kinds – straight-sided round pots and shallow pedestal-shaped pots, and their first users were druggists, dentists, and packers of bear's grease. Of one design – Waller's (plate 1) – there are five or six examples in the Guildford Museum, Surrey, and one in the Museum of the Pharmaceutical Society, London; which suggests that they were made in some numbers. Jesse Waller, a Quaker apothecary, had a shop in the High Street, Guildford, in the later years of the eighteenth century and the early years of the nineteenth.

The Waller pot is unusual, though not unique, in coming from outside London. Most known eighteenth-century pots were used by London traders (and presumably made in London, at the Lambeth potteries) for specific products. A straight-sided blue-and-white jar in the Wellcome Historical Medical Museum, London, is inscribed with the name and address of the firm that used it:

London, Manufactory  
STEWART, N° 12 & 13  
Broad Street

There are clues to the date and the original contents of this jar: street-numbering was not compulsory in London until 1767, and a newspaper cutting marked in ink with the date 1777 contains an advertisement for the product of Stewart's manufactory – his 'famous Crescent, or growing Pomade for the hair, well known to be the only thing yet heard of for restoring decayed hair. . .' A somewhat similar pot in the Museum of the Pharmaceutical Society, for Valle, 21 Hay

Market (London, *c.* 1771), still holds its original contents – a dark treacly-looking substance which no layman could identify (and few would be tempted to buy) today.

The pedestal pot used *c.* 1770 for Singleton's eye ointment (plate 2), also to be seen in the Pharmaceutical Society's Museum, was to prove one of the longest-lasting shapes in packaging. The ointment was first made in 1596 by Dr Thomas Johnson, a noted physician of the time; nobody knows what kind of container Johnson used for it, but it *is* known that in the late eighteenth century the same ointment was being sold by T. Singleton in the shallow blue-and-white pots which were to stay in use with little change for a century and a half. It is worth digressing to follow the fortunes of this pack in its exceptionally long career: from Miss Singleton who became Mrs Folgham the recipe for the ointment passed, on the marriage of Mrs Folgham's daughter Selina in 1825, to her husband, a Mr Stephen Green, who was by trade a potter. The continued manufacture of eye ointment must however have been more than a sideline for him, for the recipe was an important part of the marriage settlement, and in 1832 he brought an action – successfully – against 'certain parties [who] had imitated the Pots and counterfeited the printed Directions'. It is reasonable to assume that most if not all of the pots for Singleton's eye ointment between 1826 and 1858 were made at Green's own Lambeth pottery. After its fires had been damped down for the last time, similar pots were made first by Doulton, also of Lambeth; then by Graves of Portobello, Scotland; and finally by Kirkhams of Stoke-on-Trent. By changing suppliers when need be, Green's successors were able to keep the old design current throughout the nineteenth century and indeed until 1949: the pedestal foot of the pot became smaller with the years but the colour scheme remained unchanged. The decade in which the health of the nation became National Health saw Singleton's eye-ointment pot replaced by a glass jar with plastic top: the product was still in demand 353 years after it was introduced.

Early examples of packs for products other than ointment, paste or dentifrice are rare. The Fitzwilliam Museum, Cambridge, has the earliest known bear's grease pot (*c.* 1750)[1] which is also the first ceramic package with a picture on it – the picture of a bear. The inscription reads: 'Prepared by T. Townshend and sold only by C. King Chymist Hay Market'; Thomas Townshend was himself Chymist in Ordinary to George II.

Wyatt's pot for prepared mustard is illustrated (plate 3), and a jar for soy (a Chinese pickle) was recorded by Geoffrey Eliot Howard in his book, *Early English Drug Jars*. It was used by 'G. Searle. Druggist. Leeds', who was in business in Briggate in the first decade of the nineteenth century; the specimen once in the Howard collection was sold during the 1930s to an American drug firm also called Searle.

# Transfer-printing

BLUE and white pots with the user's name hand-lettered on them, and the even homelier brownish stoneware vessels (page 36), were all very well for some firms, especially in those trades in which it was no crime to look old-fashioned. But a new age of new products sold country-wide

---

[1] Noted by Agnes Lothian in the *Connoisseur Year Book*; see bibliography.

under known names was just around the corner, and in this new age there would have been little scope for pottery which had to be decorated entirely by hand.

Fortunately, a new method of decoration had been developed – transfer-printing, the answer to the problem which quantity production implied. This distinctively English process had its origin in Liverpool in the second half of the eighteenth century; and, unlike painting by hand, it made possible the repetition, for a virtually unlimited number of times, of a uniform design.

The designs which were to be applied to pottery were printed on sheets of specially prepared paper from engraved copper plates. (Later, lithographic stones were also used.) From the paper they were transferred to the surface of the pot at the unglazed 'biscuit' stage: the colour (or colours) stayed on when the paper was washed off. Hardening kilns burned out the oil from the inks but left behind the metallic oxides, and finally glazing fixed the colours, to last as long as the pots of which they virtually became a part.

Transfer-printed wording and decorations are first seen in packaging on early nineteenth-century jars for Crosse & Blackwell's chutney (plate 5) and Fribourg & Treyer's snuff. The latter firm still possesses several round and square snuff jars of this period (plate 4): on all of these, the elaborate lettering and the still more elaborate flourishes that accompany it are identical. From such a degree of uniformity it is evident that the jars were transfer-printed.

The best-remembered packages thus produced by the combined skills of printers (in a specialized sense) and potters were, however, the round pots with flat or slightly domed lids, transfer-printed with pictorial designs, which were made in the Staffordshire Potteries from the 1840s onwards (plates 11-17). These lids have in recent years become collectors' items, and they have their own recorded history in H. G. Clarke's *Centenary Pot-lid Book*. 'Dame Fashion prescribed that the head should be larded with a pomatum, or bear's grease', he wrote; 'and the early pots whose lids figure largely in [his] book were used to hold and embellish these preparations.' Untempting as bear's grease may seem as a hair-cream today, it founded the fortunes of at least one famous business – James Atkinson's. He not only had a bear depicted on his pot lids but used a most distinguished piece of display material, a figure of a bear made for him in the Potteries by Wood & Caldwell (1790–1818); and in his advertisements the picture of a bear, with Atkinson's name draped round it, was printed from a wood-block by Thomas Bewick, or one of Bewick's assistants (plates 8–10). Such enterprise deserved to establish a name that would last – as Atkinson's has done.

From the first transfer-printing of pottery, which was in black or a single colour, it was a relatively short step to transfer-printing in several colours: a step that was evidently approved by enterprising packers of bear's grease and other pastes and ointment, since many of them adopted multicoloured lids in the 1850s and afterwards. Some of these lids bore the name and address of the manufacturer who used them; others, only a general indication of the nature of the contents; others, again, had a picture unaccompanied by wording. But there is plenty of evidence to show that they were all used as commercial packaging even though some were completely innocent of words or symbols that could be regarded as advertising matter.

The most elaborate of the mid-nineteenth-century pot lids required for their printing four colour plates and a key plate which was printed in brown. The best-known makers were F. and

R. Pratt & Co of Fenton, Staffordshire, and their staff designer for many years was Jesse Austin. (He left them for one year, *c.* 1861, but was lured back by the offer of a salary of £175 a year. Later he reached £200.) Customers included such rising London firms as Crosse & Blackwell (plates 16 and 173), Lazenby, Burgess, and Gosnell (plate 17). John Burgess & Son used a Jesse Austin design which showed Shakespeare's birthplace with a pageant taking place in the street in front. The firm's name and address appeared on the body of the jar, but the lid was given over to art for art's sake, or Shakespeare's – not, directly, Burgess's. They also used another pot lid, printed with wording in black only, for their anchovy paste.

Among other users of transfer-printed pot lids, a small and active though unlikely-seeming group were the shrimpers of Pegwell Bay, a small village on the Kent coast near Ramsgate. The shrimping trade in this village was at its most prosperous between 1847 and 1875, the period when the output of many-coloured lids was also at its peak; and at least eighteen views of Pegwell Bay and district, including pictures of the packers' own premises, appeared on the pot lids of local firms, notably Sam Banger – who also made shrimp sauce – and Tatnell & Son.

In at least one instance, transfer-printed pots brought export business to a Staffordshire pottery – an order from H.P. & W.C. Taylor, perfumers, of Philadelphia, who commissioned pot-lids in England in two different pictorial designs, both American in their subject-matter. One design showed 'Washington crossing the Delaware', the other a prairie scene from a painting, 'An Indian buffalo hunt', by George Catlin (1796–1872), an artist who specialized in American-Indian scenes (plates 14, 15). According to H. G. Clarke, these pots were in all probability made for Taylors' stand at the Philadelphia Exhibition of 1876 – the Centennial Exposition, which was visited by eight million people and commemorated a hundred years of American independence from Britain – independence in government if not in the supply of pot-lids.

This was an age of great exhibitions: three years earlier, Crosse & Blackwell's pottery packs displayed at the Vienna Universal Exhibition had been the subject of favourable comment in the newspapers. The *Morning Post* correspondent commented: 'The very pots and jars which contain the condiments and preserves are of such an exceedingly tasteful nature, and of such exquisite Greek and Etruscan patterns, that they serve not inaptly for table ornaments, and are indeed freely used for that purpose'. The *Deutsche Zeitung* (10 July 1873) also praised the quality of the firm's products and 'their handsome and costly exterior, so artistically designed, and made in many instances of the finest Wedgwood porcelain. One would almost think, if the contrary were not so well known, that the vases, and not the contents, were the first consideration with that house...' Whether that last sentence was written with tongue in cheek, who shall say? But the reference to Wedgwood was no newspaper exaggeration: Wedgwood's records show that they sold pickle jars in blue-and-white jasper ware to Crosse & Blackwell at 2*s* 6*d* each. Such expensive (for those days) jars would not have been used for run-of-the-mill packaging but were probably reserved for special contents on special occasions, when the name of Wedgwood, and the fact that the containers had *not* been designed as commercial packaging material, gave an extra piquancy to the pickle within.

Crosse & Blackwell thus provide a notable example of the gift pack which goes against the rules of everyday packaging in that it does not display the name of the firm whose products it contains, and the customer (usually) knows that he is paying a little extra for it. There have been countless other examples since: to quote only one, from France in 1904, the Chocolaterie de la Marquise de Sévigné at Royat in the Auvergne listed in its catalogue several little pots or jugs, including some in traditional Auvergnat style, filled with a selection of bonbons, at prices from 10 to 50 francs.

THE ATTENTION which has been given to pictorial pot-lids by admirers of Victoriana must not obscure the fact that before, during and after their heyday, other methods of marking containers were used besides transfer-printing. One of these revived the Roman practice of stamping wording into wet clay; but, whereas the Romans had used engraved stone tablets for their stamps, the nineteenth-century potters, in some cases at least, used printers' type or stereos made from type.

Type-stamped inscriptions appeared on pots for products as diverse as varnish (plate 24) Crosse & Blackwell's preserves (plate 23), and Guinness's Dublin Stout (22). (Stephen Green, already mentioned for his eye-ointment pots, made leadless-glazed stout jars *c.* 1850–1858.)

Another method of making pottery into packaging was to use plain jars and stick paper labels on them. This method was widely used by early nineteenth-century blacking manufacturers, and for once we can read a first-hand account of the processes involved, written by someone who, as a boy in 1824, had worked in Warren's Jet Blacking warehouse near Charing Cross. His tasks were

> to cover the pots of paste-blacking; first with a piece of oil-paper, and then with a piece of blue paper; to tie them round with a string; and then to clip the paper close and neat, all round, until it looked as smart as a pot of ointment from an apothecary's shop. When a certain number of grosses of pots had attained this pitch of perfection, I was to paste on each a printed label, and then go on again with more pots.

The boy who did this wrapping and labelling was Charles Dickens, then twelve years old.

A pot like those which he described, and dating from only a few years later, is illustrated (plate 6): G. Lamerte, whose name appears on it, was a relative of Dickens who had bought out Jonathan Warren *c.* 1820. The prominence of the street number in the label is an oddity to be seen on the labels of Day & Martin's blacking pots also, and later on their embossed tin lids (plate 130). Theirs were taller pots than Lamerte's, and I suspect it is a Day & Martin pot that can be seen, sketched in outline, in Phil May's cartoon of a London shoeblack of 1896.

Some, at least, of the pots that Dickens labelled were made at a Lambeth pottery which was later to become famous – as recorded in *Royal Doulton 1815–1965* by Desmond Eyles. The origins of this pottery can be traced back to a certain Jones family who were making blacking pots and other stoneware at Vauxhall Walk in 1812. The first recorded Mr Jones had died before this date; his potter son Edward had slipped out of the back window and gone to South America to avoid some trouble with the law; his widow Martha was running the business. In 1815 she decided to take two employees, John Watts and John Doulton, into partnership, and for several years the partners turned out quantities of beer bottles, oil bottles, paste pots, ointment pots and drug phials.

# MATERIALS

Martha Jones retired in February 1820 and the ex-employees continued the business. Their account book for 1835 is a valuable guide to London firms who were packaging in pottery before Victoria came to the throne; their customers at that time included Whitbread of Whitechapel, brewers; Berger of Homerton and Pinchin & Johnson of Ratcliffe, paintmakers; Seager, Evans & Co of Millbank, distillers; Crosse & Blackwell who bought jam jars of various sizes; Stephens who bought stoneware ink-bottles, and the makers of Warren's blacking, one of Doulton & Watts' three biggest customers. In 1896 Doulton & Co were still making blacking bottles, though they were better known by then for other things.

# (2)
# GLASS

GLASSMAKING was one of the civilized skills that our uncivilized ancestors allowed to die out when the Romans left Britain in the first century A.D. Little or no glass was made here for the next thousand years, and there was no bottle-making industry of any consequence until Sir Robert Mansell, an admiral, forsaking one kind of vessel for another, acquired control of some thirty glass-houses in different parts of Britain, through a grant of letters patent from King James I in 1623.

Soon after this, glass bottles began to replace stoneware as serving vessels for wine in private houses and in inns. Many innkeepers (and many families also) had their bottles marked with their initials, and some, most conveniently for us, with the date as well: the marking was done by stamping a seal of glass – otherwise known as a pad, prunt, button, or label. The stamping was effected while the glass was still warm, before it had completely hardened, rather as sealing wax is marked with a signet (the seal was usually on the shoulder of the bottle and did *not* seal it in the sense of closing it). The earliest known example with a date, 1657, shows a head in profile and the initials R.P.M. (plate 25); it was probably made for a King's Head tavern, but how it was used is uncertain. Glass must be considered as a packaging material from the time when innkeepers began to send out bottles of wine to their customers as well as using bottles to serve wine on their own premises but unfortunately no historian has recorded the date when this happened.

It may well have happened first in the university towns of Oxford and Cambridge. Samuel Pepys' diary records that, at a supper party in Cambridge in 1660, he 'caused two bottles of wine to be carried from the Rose Tavern'; and a bottle now in the Fitzwilliam Museum is marked CAMBRIDG. E.C. 1684: probably 'E.C.' indicated E. Clarke, who was landlord of the Dolphin Tavern about this time. A rotund Oxford bottle of about 1700 was dug up by workmen engaged on alterations to the Randolph Hotel, Oxford, in 1950 (plate 26), and there is a duplicate of it, as well as a fragment of a third example, in the Ashmolean Museum.

For the keen commercial man, marking his bottles with a seal was a rather inconspicuous way of putting his name on them. It was used to some extent in America (plates 27, 28) as well as in Britain, but enterprising traders everywhere soon began to look for ways of marking their glass packages more prominently and with more lengthy wording than the form of a seal would allow. There were two possible courses which they could take; one was to have the name moulded in the body of the glass (if the trader could afford to pay for a mould), and the other was to use printed paper labels. Lady Ruggles-Brise[1] notes, among the earliest examples of moulded

[1] In *Sealed Bottles*: see bibliography.

This bottle, with its elaborate moulded decoration above and round the label, was illustrated in an advertisement in the diamond jubilee number of the *Illustrated London News*, 1897

lettering, two bottles of 1733 and 1735 bearing the name of T. Smith, a chemist, of Salisbury, Wiltshire, which were probably made to contain tinctures. A more famous name moulded in the glass of many bottles is TRUE DAFFY'S MIXTURE or TRUE DAFFY'S ELIXIR; this remedy for gout and rheumatism was in favour from the middle of the seventeenth century until well into the nineteenth – at one time with a coat of arms stamped in the wax seal on the cork, at one time with a label designed by Thomas Bewick.

Of course, it was not only wording that could be moulded in glass; decoration could be added, and by the second half of the nineteenth century the craft of mould-making was so highly developed as to make possible a bottle for Rose's lime juice in which the surface was almost covered by trailing decorative limes and leaves – almost but not quite, because there was a label to be added as well.

As USERS of paper labels, the eighteenth-century patent medicine vendors were probably in advance of the vintners; labelled drug phials (in the Wellcome Museum, for example; plate 30) are probably older than any labelled wine bottles. Indeed, only two examples of the latter are recorded before the end of the century: the Companhia Geral of the Douro valley in Portugal used a simple black-and-white paper label to identify its new 'fortified' port wine in 1756, and another was applied, in Germany, to the 1775 vintage bottles of Rüdesheimer Berg.

It is likely that by the end of the eighteenth century Burgess's essence of anchovies (plate 37) and Lazenby's Harvey's sauce were on the market in labelled bottles not noticeably different from those in which they were to enter the twentieth: soon there were enough proprietary sauces to disprove the Continental accusation that in England there were sixty different religions and only one sauce. By their nature sauces were suitable for packaging in glass; of necessity they required descriptive labels; and by happy chance these labels were often notable for their handsome engraved designs (plates 35-36).

IN THE LATE seventeenth century England exported bottles to Europe: in the eighteenth, this trade was harder to get as new bottle works were established on the Continent – especially in the Netherlands; the Dutch, *c.* 1760, made bottles for the Constantia vineyard in their colony in South Africa, as well as for their home market.

# GLASS

The mid-eighteenth century saw the beginnings, nevertheless, of two concerns which were still active in bottle-making 200 years later – the Alloa Glass Work, now part of United Glass Ltd but originally a group of glassworkers from Bohemia who settled in the Forth estuary on the invitation of Lady Erskine of Mar (1750); and John Wright & Co (now Beatson, Clark & Co Ltd) of Rotherham, Yorkshire. One of Wright's first products was a bottle for Robert Turlington's 'invented Balsom of Life/London/Jany. 26 1754'. The widespread and lasting distribution of this commodity is evident from the discovery of some bottles in North American Indian graves of half a century later.

In the West of England, the eighteenth century saw the development of bottle-making at Bristol, not only for local beer, cider and perry but for export to Ireland, the West Indies and the American colonies. Later, in 1811, what had once been known as the Soap-boilers' Glass House was purchased by Jacob Wilcox Ricketts, his son Henry, and two others. The name of H. RICKETTS & CO. GLASS WORKS, BRISTOL, is found moulded in the glass of many bottles, some now in the Sheffield City Museum, some in America – for one of Ricketts' customers was the New York firm of Bininger, tea and wine merchants established in 1778. The bottles which Ricketts made for them, probably in the 1820s, were of heavy olive-green glass with BININGER. NEW YORK encircling a bunch of grapes on a seal; it would be interesting to know what advantages of price or style or quality Ricketts were able to offer, to tempt a New York merchant to buy his bottles such a long sea journey away.

America had a glass industry of her own by this time, as she had had, on a small scale, since Colonial days; and most of the early American glass-houses had been obliged to make such utilitarian products as bottles or window-glass – or go out of business. In the early 1750s such a glass-house was established at Quincy, Massachusetts, using immigrant German labour to make bottles for shipping New England cider to the West Indies. Re-established after a fire in 1755, this Germantown glass-house made snuff bottles, wide-mouthed jars for pickles and conserves, and chemical vessels.

Snuff and mustard bottles were advertised in the next decade by Richard Wistar, son of Caspar Wistar (d. 1752), who had been the first successful glass-maker in North America; and in the 1780s, bottles were being made at the Pitkin and the Olive glass-works: the latter was to have a long history, ending as a part of the Owens company, a famous name in the next century.

An early American medicine bottle which still exists has the inscription DR ROBERTSON'S/ FAMILY MEDICINE/PREPARED ONLY BY T. W. DYOTT. This bottle is the subject of one of the 3,000 illustrations in George and Helen McKearin's encyclopaedic book on *American Glass*; and it introduces us to one of the most colourful characters in the history of packaging. Thomas Dyott arrived in America as a poor boy in 1795, and was soon in business as a maker of shoe-blacking. Next he went into the patent medicine business, and by 1812 he was calling himself T. W. Dyott, M.D. Soon he moved over from the package-user's to the package-maker's side of the fence, at first as an agent for the Olive glass-works, later as head of Dyottville Works at Kensington, Philadelphia. It was during his palmy days as Dyott of Dyottville that the moulded pictorial bottles now known as 'historical flasks' (*e.g.* plate 29) were in vogue in America, and Dyott was the only bottle-maker with the nerve to put his own portrait on a bottle – opposite Benjamin

Franklin's. The business was successful until a widespread financial panic in 1837 tempted Dyott to cook the books of a bank which he had established, and he was convicted of fraudulent bankruptcy.

Later in the century, two American pioneers of branded goods, I. W. Lyon and Gerhard Mennen (both of whom are better known as early users of metal boxes – see page 79) packaged their wares in glass bottles: Lyon's tooth powder in 1874, Mennen's Sure Corn Killer, the first product which he advertised and sold through other druggists' shops as well as his own, a few years later. According to his biographer, Mennen placed too much faith in the bottle-makers: in 1879, his corn-killer sold so fast that he ran out of bottles at the height of the summer and found that the manufacturers had closed down for holidays and the bottle merchants had no stock left of the size he needed.

We get a clear indication of the growing volume of American packaging business from the correspondence of another old-established firm, the Bernardin Bottle Cap Co of Evansville, Indiana. In 1896, one of their customers, the Anheuser-Busch Brewing Association of St Louis, placed a repeat order for half-a-million caps for beer bottles, 100,000 to be delivered at once, and the rest at the rate of 50,000 weekly. Evidently the brewers did not intend to be caught out by their suppliers as the young and inexperienced Mennen had been.

THERE was relatively little development in methods of bottle-making between the invention of the blowpipe, about the time of Christ, and the nineteenth century. Most bottles need to be wider at the closed end than at the open end – in other words, to have narrow necks – and, while this presented no problem for the glass-blower, it was a major obstacle to the use of mechanized aids in bottle-making. For a long time it was the practice for the necks of quantity-produced bottles to be made separately from the bodies, and stuck on like spouts on teapots; not until 1821 was a split mould patented (by Ricketts of Bristol) which enabled body and neck to be made together.

Even then, mechanization of bottle-making was still some way off. Progress awaited recognition of the fact that a bottle machine would need to 'start with the finish', i.e. to make the neck before the body. A patent application by Philip Arbogast of Pittsburgh in 1881 showed that he had grasped the fact: he wrote of 'pressing the mouth or neck to finished form with a dependent mass of glass, then withdrawing the plunger, then removing the article from the press mould, and finally inserting it in a separate mould and blowing to form the body'. For a variety of reasons, Arbogast's methods were never used very widely – though they were employed in 1893 by a licensee of the patent, the Enterprise Glass Company, for making Vaseline jars.

It was at Ferrybridge, Yorkshire, that the first moderately successful semi-automatic machine, with two separate moulds, was invented by Josiah C. Arnall, a postman, and Howard M. Ashley (who had never worked in a glassworks). Patents were granted to Ashley in 1886, '87 and '89, and with machines of his design two men could produce 1,200 bottles a day. Ashley machines were in use in Britain and in the United States, where they were known as Johnny Bulls, until 1915–16.

By this time, the inevitable step from semi-automatic to automatic bottle-making had been taken by Michael Joseph Owens of Toledo, Ohio. He conceived the basic idea of his machine in 1899; it involved a device like a bicycle pump – outsize and heatproof – which on one stroke would suck in molten glass to form the neck of a bottle, and on the next stroke would blow out air, to force enough of this glass down into the larger end of the mould to form the body.

By 1903 further development had convinced Owens that automatic bottle-making was practicable, and the Owens Bottle Machine Company was formed. In the firm's first production model, the Owens No. 5 machine, the 'gathering' mould dipped into molten glass as the machine revolved. It was – as has been said of early Rolls-Royce cars – a triumph of craftmanship over design: its method of working entailed the raising and lowering of ten tons of machinery for every gathering of glass. But it was successful, vastly increasing the speed at which bottles could be made and bringing progress in a human as well as a technical sense, for bottle-making by hand had entailed a 'waste of human life. . . . It was one of the most exhausting and dangerous, in the slow as apart from the sudden sense, of trades', in the words of a contemporary writer in *Truth*. Owens revolutionized the bottle industry – and not only the American bottle industry; in 1907 the first Owens machines in Europe were installed in Germany by a British company (Apollinaris & Johannis Ltd) which bottled the waters of the Apollinaris spring.

Known as the 'Hamilton' from its inventor (in 1814), this type of bottle had to lie flat; thus its cork was kept moist, and the aerated water stayed aerated. A Schweppe bottle like the one illustrated (used between 1845 and 1880) is in the Hertford Museum: Poole and Tunbridge Wells museums have similar bottles from other firms, and at least one from Britain is in the possession of the Glass Container Manufacturers Institute Inc

WHEN YOU HAVE MADE your bottle, whether by hand or by machine, you still have the problem of how to close it; a problem to which cork was for a long time the best if not the only answer. Tight-fitting corks made sparkling champagne possible in France. In England, early ale bottles had their corks firmly held in place by string or wire – and the effectiveness of these closures was to be proved by two centuries of English weather, for in 1953 a great storm exposed some eighteenth-century bottles in sand on the Kent coast, with the corks still in position and strong ale inside.

# MATERIALS

So long as corks had to be fitted by hand, even with mechanical aids, bottling was bound to be a slow process, and this eventually led to the brewers' abandonment of corks in favour of screw stoppers (introduced in 1872) and Crown caps (invented in 1891 by William Painter of Baltimore; made in the United States from 1892 onwards, in England from 1897).

Meanwhile, for 'soft' drinkers, the mineral-water bottle with a glass marble in its neck had been invented by Hiram Codd of Camberwell in the 1870s (plate C). It was to flourish for half-a-century or more, and large numbers of marble-in-the-neck bottles still exist: enough to show how widely they were used in their heyday. I have seen examples in museums at King's Lynn, Cambridge, Hertford, Rye, Poole, Monmouth. . . . Some of the moulded designs have an unexpected richness of detail, depicting, for example, the arms of the borough of Poole for the Dorset Mineral Water Co and a local sailing ship for Colebrook of Rye.

There is a nostalgic reference to the Codd type of bottle in Christopher Morley's novel *Thorofare*, which has its setting about the time of Queen Victoria's jubilee:

'I'd rather have lemonade with a marble in it', said Geoffrey. He meant one of those bottles of Ipswich lemon soda in which the impatience of the gas kept a glass marble stoppered in the neck. The publican, whose eyes also looked like wet marbles, drove a wooden peg into the neck of the bottle and with a conjurer's quickness received the jetting foam in a tall glass.

Among souvenirs of a forgotten world perhaps Geoffrey would most cherish one of those empty bottles, with the glass ball tingling inside. Like the crystal globule of youth, once the pressure was loosed the marble fell into a slot in the neck of the bottle, irretrievable.

Nineteenth-century style in the twentieth century. The carton for the Kepler bottle is illustrated on page 33. The wrapper which envelops a Horlick's bottle was in use in 1908 when the firm's British factory came into operation; before that, Horlick's malted milk had been shipped in bulk from Racine, Wisconsin (where it was invented by William Horlick in 1883), and packed in a London warehouse

# (3)
# PAPER
# and foil: bags & wrappers

PAPER, the most versatile of all packaging materials, came on to the scene in the most undignified way – as a second-hand material. In seventeenth-century London, books which failed to sell as reading matter were sent to Bucklersbury, where the grocers and apothecaries had their shops, to be sold off as wrapping paper – a change of use that was less difficult then than now because the books in seventeenth-century bookshops were stocked in sheet form, unfolded and unbound till someone came along and bought them.

Earlier still, in the mid-sixteenth century when the 'popish elements' were removed from England's churches, the villagers of Wrangle in Lincolnshire are said to have torn up their service-books to make 'papars thereof to wrappe spice in'. About the same time, in Germany, which was possibly more civilized and certainly more advanced in the paper trades than sixteenth-century Britain, the Brunswick papermaker, Bernhart, began packing his paper in a wrapper with a printed design on it. The method of papermaking in use at that time left dregs in the bottom of the vat which were not good enough to make saleable writing or printing paper but could be used for coarser brown or grey paper in which to wrap it. Bernhart added identification to protection by printing his wrapping-paper with a lively woodcut of a horse (which was also his watermark), a shield, and his name and address – *Andreas Bernhart, Papiermacher auff der Ocker* (plate 45). Dard Hunter, from whose book on *Papermaking*[1] Bernhart's printed wrapper is reproduced, believed that similar 'paper-package labels' had been used as early as the *fifteenth* century, though he does not appear to have found any first-hand evidence to support this view. It is of course known that paper was being printed from wood blocks before 1450.

In Bernhart's day, or soon afterwards, one Italian trader – a silk merchant, perhaps – was also using printed paper labels, but it is uncertain whether these were stuck on the material or on paper in which it was wrapped – and it might be stretching definitions to regard the former as packaging. Gaspare Pagni's label (plate 46) depicted a street scene in the Merzaria, the oldest shopping street in Venice. The picture had a broad border of birds and foliage – a border in which it may not be too fanciful to see some influence from textile design: block-printing was used for the decoration of fabrics even before it was applied to paper. Pagni's address is printed on the label as ALL' INSEGNA DEL LORETO IN MERZARIA IN VENETIA. Such descriptive addresses were common at the time, and were to remain useful for many years, until the practice of street-numbering in all the larger towns made them unnecessary.

[1] See bibliography.

IN THE SEVENTEENTH century, London was not only the country's outstanding centre of fashion and smart shops, as it is today, but also of manufacture and invention, in a way that it has never been since the Industrial Revolution: there may well have been English pioneers of paper packaging who lost their stock, their premises and their prospects, when the wind blew hot from Pudding Lane and Samuel Pepys 'saw all the towne burned': we may never know. But one man lost £20,000 worth of tobacco, and a Westminster schoolboy, William Taswell, noted in his diary for 1666 that 'papers, half burnt, were carried with the wind to Eton' – well over twenty miles from London.

In the sixty years before the Great Fire, all sorts of new luxuries had appeared on the scene – several of them products which may well have been paper-wrapped. Tea reached Europe in 1614; coffee was on sale in Oxford in 1648; a coffee-house opened in London in 1652; drinking-chocolate came a few years later; and only a year before the fire, in 1665, the first British patent for papermaking was granted to Charles Hildegard or Hildeyerd – for 'the way and art of making blew paper used by sugar-bakers . . .'

Some manufacturers of patent medicines were already packaging their wares for recognition as well as physical protection: in the *Mercurius Politicus* of November 1660, Mr Theophilus Buckworth advertised his 'so famous *Lozenges* or *Pectorals* . . . for the cure of Consumption, Coughs, Catarrhs [and almost everything else]; for more convenience of the people' they were available at five addresses 'sealed up with his coat of arms on the papers'. In the following month another advertiser, Robert Turner, Gentleman, announced that his Dentifrices were only to be bought 'in sealed papers, at 12*d* the paper'.

# Tobacco papers and trade cards

In the century after the Fire of London, there was a general shortage of paper. Little except the coarsest grades was yet made in England, still less in North America. But before 1800 paper packs were an accepted part of the shopping scene: packs for playing cards, tea, sago powder, pins (plate A) and tobacco. Perhaps tobacco papers are the best-known of these: there are examples in the Guildhall Library, London, and in the Banks collection in the British Museum. Happily for the historian, one of the few dated examples is probably one of the earliest, Thomas Lacy's (plate 47). It has this wording:

*Patriae prodest*
Thos Lacy Tobacco Merchant
in Martins Lane by Cannon street
London 1669

There is no special significance in the patriotic sentiment of Mr Lacy's first line. '*PRO-PATRIA*' appeared on a Dutch papermaker's wrapper of a slightly later date: and the royal arms were used, to indicate loyalty no doubt, but without any royal authority for their use, in many eighteenth- and nineteenth-century package designs – as they were used on the front page of *The Times* until 1966.

# PAPER

F. W. Fairholt, in his *History of Tobacco* published in 1876, stated that the fashion of 'giving "something literary" on tobacco-papers was very customary about twenty years ago, and embraced a large variety of topics'. It was; and a good deal earlier too. Through the eighteenth and nineteenth centuries, tobacconists – or their printers – concocted a steady stream of jokes, riddles and rhymes: the deathless verse below appeared on the tobacco paper of Joseph Haynes, Little Eastcheap:

> This Plant Produc'd by Industry and Pains
> Is sold for Publick Good by me Jo. Haynes.

Tobacco papers, like epitaphs in country churchyards, have a quaintness in twentieth-century eyes that tempts one to go on quoting them for quaintness' sake. The temptation must be resisted: what is more interesting is to note how international the characteristics of early tobacco papers were. The claim that the contents were the best in the world appeared on several British and Continental papers, with *Petum optimum subter solem* translated into the vernacular for the benefit of the less scholarly smokers (or users of tobacco in other ways: it might be smoked, chewed, or taken as snuff at this time). Similar papers were used in eighteenth-century Britain and eighteenth-century Holland (plates 48 to 51) and in a range of Norwegian tobacco packs that was still current in the second half of the nineteenth century (plate 52). One of these packs, from Tiedeman[n] of Christiania – now Oslo – was for a blend of tobacco with the very English-sounding name of 'Wagstaff's Superfine'.

Tobacconists in the seventeenth and eighteenth centuries were retail shopkeepers who made-up their own blends and weighed out the tobacco into the wrapping paper while the customer waited. In most other trades, too, it was the retailer who took the initiative in packaging – though some retailers were also manufacturers, selling their wares in the front room, making and packing them in the back room. A paper wrapper for Bowens Patent Sago Powder (plate 53) in the Victoria & Albert Museum, London, shows an unusually highly organized state of trade for its day, *c.* 1780: Bowen was presumably the manufacturer; Stringer & Leach were named as sole wholesalers, and the product reached its consumers through a number of retail grocers' shops.

But this is the exception, not the rule: the shopkeeper was the man who commissioned most package designs. Not all of them were exclusively *package* designs, for in the eighteenth century the moderately progressive trader (catering no doubt for the nobility and gentry – most other customers could not read) had a single piece of printed matter, the trade card, which was his business stationery, his advertising matter and, in some trades, his package also. The name of 'trade card' is misleading, for the 'cards' were, in fact, sheets of stout paper. In the Heal collection there is such a card, used by Edward Eagleton, who founded his tea business in the City of London in 1771, with this wording: 'ALL TEAS &c sold by me, will be packed in fine paper, with my name and catalogue printed, and the price marked on each parcel. . . .' Then follows a list; from which it is evident that Eagleton's trade card *was* his catalogue, and logical to suppose that it was also the 'fine paper' in which his tea was packed.

The 200-year-old London firm of Reeves, artists' colourmen, provides first-hand evidence of yet another use of trade cards – as labels: Reeves used to stick the cards inside the lids of plain wooden boxes in which their paints were sold (plate 54) as a means of identification and, incidentally, decoration.

# Nineteenth-century paper wrappers

SOME tobacco papers and trade cards were printed from type only, some from type and wood blocks, some from engraved copper plates: those which still exist suggest that in the eighteenth century engraved designs (e.g. plate 49) were in the majority. And, despite the development of

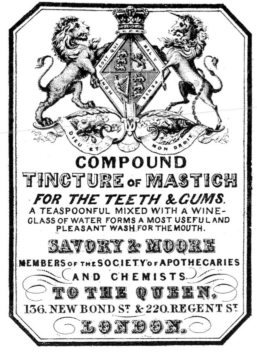

Royal arms in various styles on nineteenth-century English labels. The label for Seidlitz powders shows the signature of the engraver, H. Silverlock (London, c. 1859). The Tincture of Mastich label is of the same period; the pin paper of the 'nineties, for D. F. Tayler

52

new printing techniques in the next century, engraving continued to be widely used – with steel plates available as an alternative to copper. Though the earliest known American papermaker's label was printed from a wood block, as already noted on page 26, some notable later labels for the same industry were engravings: e.g. those for T. Gilpin & Co, Brandywine, c. 1810, and for the Elijah Burbank paper mill at Worcester, Mass., c. 1825.

In England in the 1840s, pin papers for a Bristol pin manufacturer – a Quaker, Robert Charlton – were printed by a local copperplate printer, John Harris. 'Mr Charlton supplied his own paper which was tinted . . ., well made, and tough, to stand folding so as to take the rows of pins which would be stuck in. Each customer had his own special design, and these were engraved on steel, and occupied the centre of the sheet. . . . The paper, as far as memory now serves me, was about 30 inches long by 12 inches wide and, to be printed from the plate, had to be folded to allow the label to come in the centre. . . . When the order had been completed, Charlton's carter would call for it and take the papers to a book-binder (John Holland), who would . . . gild all the edges, and have them ready for the carter when he brought the next lot.' This eye-witness account of methods which cannot have been very different from those of the eighteenth century was written in 1918 by Heber Mardon, whose father had taken over the pin-paper printing business from John Harris in the 1850s. Bridging two centuries in fact and three in spirit, Mardon's reminiscences confirm one's view that the plate printer rather than the letterpress printer is the true ancestor of today's mass-production package-printing industries.

MARBLED PAPER, used in bookbinding on the Continent since the seventeenth century, is first mentioned as a packaging material in the 1800s, when it was used for Dr James's Fever Powders. Other all-over patterned papers were introduced soon afterwards. They were employed not only as wrappers but as cover-papers pasted on boxes (plate 85), and were recommended for label-printing in De La Rue's trade catalogue of 1849. And, despite the visual appeal of coloured patterns, paper wrappers printed in black only remained popular for many kinds of merchandise: used by shopkeepers on both sides of the Atlantic (plates 61 and 62); by makers of soap (55) and butterscotch (60), and by patent-medicine vendors who decided that their glass bottles needed some additional protection – and the contents some additional advertisement (31, 58).

An Englishman visiting Paris in 1847, Tom Smith, was so impressed by the wrapping of bonbons which he saw in a shop there that he brought the idea back to England and applied it profitably to the wrapping of sugared almonds for the Christmas trade. Later, from his twists of coloured paper, he was to develop the Christmas cracker; this was Tom Smith's best-known contribution to the gaiety of nations, but *en passant* he had introduced individually wrapped sweets to the English-speaking world: a form of packaging which was soon to devour vast acreages of paper, film and foil each year.

It was probably in France that metal foil was first used for the wrapping of confectionery: we have an eye-witness account of this activity by Anatole France in his autobiographical novel *Little Pierre*. He recalled frequent visits, as a small boy in the 1840s, to the sweetshop of Debeauve & Gallais, 'chocolate makers to the Kings of France. . . . It seemed to me as though I were entering a fairy palace. . . . Young ladies, both dark and fair, were busily engaged, some in covering the

Eighteenth- and nineteenth-century versions of the Black Boy which was long a symbol of the tobacco trade, seen in shop signs as well as packaging. The more open line employed in the later version must have simplified printing

A similar design in use early in the present century on a round pack of shag tobacco (*above right*)

cakes of chocolate with a thin metal leaf of silvery brightness, others in enveloping these same cakes, two at a time, in white paper wrappers with pictures on them and then sealing these wrappers with wax which they heated in the flame of a little tin lamp. . . . It was a joy to the eye to watch the deft fingers of those young women.'

In England meanwhile, tinfoil was being used in the packaging of tea (*e.g.* by Fred. & Robt. Sparrow & Co of Ludgate Hill, *c.* 1840) and coffee. The *London Mercury* in 1848 praised the dispatch with which coffee was made up into 'very neat packages, encased in tinfoil' in the packing department at John Cassell's: this same Cassell's printing press, bought originally for the printing of his tea and coffee labels, was later to lead to the establishment of the publishing house of Cassell. Though neither Anatole France nor the *London Mercury* was there to praise them, there were no doubt deft fingers at work in the 1850s in Birmingham also, where cakes of Cadburys' drinking chocolate were wrapped in tinfoil and greaseproof paper and a printed outer wrappper of white paper.

AMONG the new lines sold in printed paper wrappers during the second half of the century were butter and margarine in the United States and cigarettes both in the States and in Britain. It was the inadequacy of paper packets as protective containers for anything as fragile as cigarettes that led to the introduction of cigarette cards, which were originally intended as stiffeners (and always known in the trade by this name). The first printed stiffeners were produced in America in 1879; the first in Britain for W. D. & H. O. Wills of Bristol by their neighbours, Mardon Son & Hall, nearly a decade later.

American margarine and American cigarettes both have a contribution to make to the folklore of packaging. In 1888, United States law required that all butter-substitutes should be wrapped in paper 'with the inscription "Margarine" printed in the largest and boldest style of type'. The *American Lithographer* reported:

> A lithographer has taken advantage of this and prints an enormous quantity of wrappers, selling to all dealers. . . . The secret of the great demand for his wrappers is that he prints a portrait of a handsome young beauty, and under the picture prints the prescribed 'Margarine' in type, the letters of which are an inch high. The joke of the matter is, ninety-nine out of a hundred people imagine 'Margarine' is the name of the pretty young damsel. We must frankly admit that this ruse of the cute lithographer beats anything yet attempted by smart advertisers in 'oleomargarine' in America.

The story of a rather more ingenuous tobacco package of the same period comes from James B. Wallace's introduction to *Howe & Hummel* by Richard Rovere:

> the horny-handed son of toil smoked Honest Long Cut. It came in a paper package, on the cover of which was the picture of a street car driver standing on the front platform of his car, driving his horses and puffing away contentedly on a corncob pipe. A passenger stood beside him on the platform, and issuing from his mouth in a little 'balloon' came the slogan "If that's Honest Long Cut, blow the smoke this way".

There is a different, but also rather folksy, packet for the same brand of tobacco in the Container Corporation's museum (plate 167).

Interesting evidence of the flow of trade across the Atlantic at this time is to be found in the *Lithographers' Directory,* published in New York in 1887–8: the advertisers included Taylor Bros, of Leeds, England, selling to the American trade 'GROCERS TEA PAPERS AND WRAPPERS, plain or in colors, in all usual sizes. Special designs supplied when required. Samples free'. The reference to 'all usual sizes' is interesting; the nineteenth was a century of very free enterprise rather than standardization but, as Taylors' advertisement suggests, there were generally recognized sizes of paper wrappers for different weights of tea (and tobacco). C. T. Jacobi listed them in his *Printers Handbook of Trade Recipes etc* in 1887; they ranged from foolscap for a pound of tea down to crown 12mo for half-an-ounce of tobacco.

# Paper bags

A TRACT[1] OF THE TIME of the Thirty Years' War (1618–48), lamenting the sorry state of contemporary Europe, complains of paper coming from the mills 'like blotting-paper, not good enough even for grocers' paper bags'. This is probably the first reference to paper bags, and it is surprising that there are no more detailed references to this homely form of package for another 200 years.

A bag is so simple to make, provided you have time and patience and rather more paper than you would expect to need, that one imagines many general printers must have branched out into bagmaking on occasions, if not as a regular practice, to oblige their shopkeeper customers.

The beginnings of an English bag-making firm have been described by Bernard Darwin.[2] In 1844 Elisha Smith Robinson, a young man whose assets included first-hand acquaintance with a paper mill and with a Cotswold village grocer's shop, and £190 capital, moved to Bristol to start his own business. At first it was largely supplying wrapping paper, in particular to the grocery trade, but soon he set seriously about making paper bags by hand. His seriousness was evidently rewarded, for he married on the strength of his first year's profits and within a few years added a small letterpress printing plant to his bag-making facilities. Later there were to be litho presses also.

Elisha Robinson's brother Alfred joined him in the firm in 1848[3] and went out as a salesman 'all through the West country as far as Penzance, breaking new ground and introducing in face of much prejudice the novel idea of ready-made paper bags. He was at once courteous and pertinacious and extremely successful'.

So, too, were his rivals in another Bristol firm: that of James Mardon (successor to the plate printer John Harris already mentioned), which began, probably in the 1850s, to strive for a share of the paper bag trade. Heber Mardon, James's son, noted that many customers in the grocery and drapery trades 'desired to have views of their premises on their billheads, bags and tea papers, more especially in South Wales. . . . where I often went to make the sketches for orders [which the local representative] had taken. Robinson's steam litho machine had not absorbed all

[1] Quoted in *Druck und Papier,* 1960, and by Long; see bibliography.

[2] See bibliography.

[3] It then became E. S. & A. Robinson. It is now (and has been since 1893) E. S. & A. Robinson Ltd.

the orders, its great use being the execution of long numbers, but there were plenty of customers with smaller orders left'.

Noting the success of Robinsons and Mardons and the existence of at least one other local commercial printer, Holloway & Son, we are tempted to think of Bristol as the capital of nine-teenth-century bag printing. Bristol firms certainly had a wide market – Robinsons made bags for customers in the North Midlands of England and the North Island of New Zealand (plates 66

Puzzle picture on a tea paper by Holloway & Son, Bristol, 1893

& 67) – but they had no monopoly; bags can be seen with the imprints of London (plate 65) and Birmingham (192) printers, and it is reasonable to suppose that local research would bring to light other bag-printing firms in Britain and in the United States.

Francis Wolle[1] of Bethlehem, Pennsylvania, developed the first paper bag-making machine in 1852; James Arkell, with his partners Benjamin and Adam Smith, patented another in 1859

[1] In 1869, Wolle and others were to form the Union Paper Bag Machine Co, which at one time (according to the *Modern Packaging Encyclopaedia*) owned or controlled the use of 90 per cent of the paper bag business in the United States.

and put it to work at Canajoharie on the Mohawk River (thus establishing what is now America's 'oldest name in paper bags' – Arkell & Smiths, of Hudson Falls, N.Y.); and Robert Gair of New York branched out into the manufacture of paper bags soon after starting in business as a paper merchant in 1864.

Gair, who had emigrated from Scotland to New York at the age of 14, was a Civil War 'veteran' of 25 when he established his business in Reade Street: Lord & Taylor and Macy's were not far away, and he was soon selling paper bags to department stores as well as small shops. At first they were plain bags, hand-made by girls, but soon Gair added second-hand treadle presses so that he could supply printed bags to his growing circle of New York customers. Seed bags and grocers' patent machine-made bags appeared in one of his early catalogues: another packaging business was well on the way to success.

The growing industry of bag-making inspired one of the few academic comments on packaging in the nineteenth century. In 1889 Professor David Ames Wells wrote, in *Recent Economic Changes*: 'Nothing has had a greater influence in making possible the rapidity with which certain branches of retail business are now conducted, as compared with ten years ago – more especially the sale of groceries – than the cheap and rapid production of paper bags. . . . Machinery has crowded out the hand workers, and factories . . . in the United States . . . produce millions of paper bags per week, and not unfrequently fill single orders for three millions.'

In 1873, Elisha Smith Robinson of Bristol paid a visit to America. He considered the New York stores thriftless and untidy, but he was favourably impressed by a machine which he saw for making bags of satchel or gusseted shape – so favourably that he bought the patent for £1,000 and came home to apply it in his own business: the first British machines were made for him by Hodges, also a Bristol firm.

Yet mechanization spread slowly, for the human machine was still the cheapest machine in many cases, and the most versatile. The story of E. S. & A. Robinson illustrates this point well; at the end of the 1880s they had five bag-making machines and by 1902 they had seventeen – but they still employed four hundred people on bag-making by hand.

Shopkeepers, as has already been noted, were important customers for paper bags (plates 63-64, 66–67) from the time bags were first made; and with the growth of department stores, they became bigger and bigger customers as the nineteenth century advanced; in the second half of the century, manufacturers in some industries found that the paper bag was the answer to their packaging problems, too. Flour milling was one of these. In America, cotton sacks had been used before the Civil War; then the war put a temporary stop to the supply of cotton and the millers were forced into packaging in paper. The bags at first available were quite unsuited to flour, but the occasion produced the man – a man who said 'I will produce a paper bag sturdy enough to carry 50 pounds of flour', and did so. He was George West, who had learnt the paper business in his native Devonshire, by now had a mill at Ballston Spa in New York State, and was later to be a close associate of Robert Gair's. Paper flour sacks and buckwheat sacks appeared in Gair's catalogue in the 1870s.

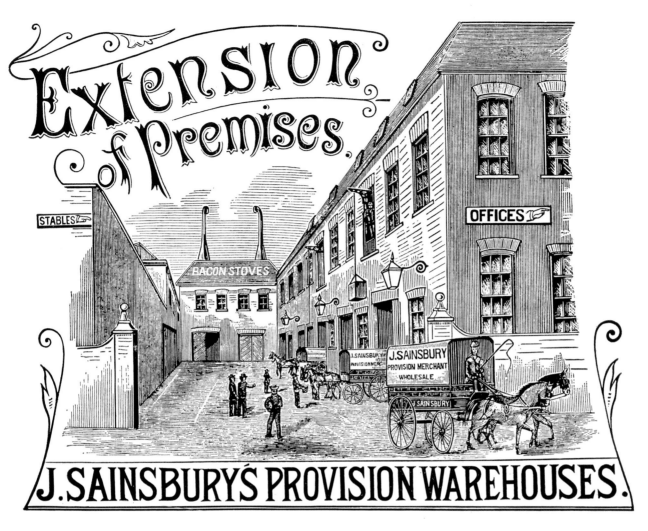

J. Sainsbury opened his first warehouse at Kentish Town, London *c.* 1880 – with stoves for smoking Irish and Canadian bacon – and illustrated it on his paper bags

In England, Bibby & Baron installed their first Rose machine for making flour bags in 1874[1] at Burnley, Lancashire. Established in 1868, they were the first of a number of Lancashire bag-makers; Joseph Chadwick & Sons started in this business at Oldham in 1873, J. S. Duxbury at Blackburn in 1877, Higham Bros at Farnworth near Bolton in 1890. The development of printing methods that would keep pace with the machine production of bags was a problem for many years; Bibby & Baron – who from their earliest days were engineers as well as bag-makers (plate 71) – took an important step towards solving it *c.* 1890, when they made and installed in their own works a press designed on the basis of a large central drum (the impression cylinder) with various printing units placed round it, and paper fed to the drum in a continuous web. It was designed to

---

[1] According to *Packaging Review*, June 1957. Rose Bros were the machinery manufacturers, later Rose Bros (Gainsborough) Ltd; now Rose Forgrove Ltd.

print with quick-drying aniline inks from rubber blocks or plates, and so can be regarded as the first *flexographic* printing press (though the vocabulary of the time was still innocent of that word, as indeed it was of 'packaging' in our present sense).

Early in the new century Robinsons installed their first combined printing and bag-making machine, devised by their own engineers, and Foster G. Robinson followed his grandfather's footsteps to America – not, however, to buy but to sell patent rights, to the Union Bag Company of New York.

Aniline inks and flexographic printing were finally assured of a future in the packaging industries by C. A. Holweg, a machinist in Alsace Lorraine, whose press (developed in 1905, patented in Britain in 1908) was designed to work in conjunction with a bag-making machine, 'with synchronization of printing and cut-off accomplished by hand'.[1] Holweg's inks were made of dyestuffs dissolved in spirits which dried so quickly that the making of the bags could follow printing as part of one continuous operation – the aim of paper bag-makers for a quarter of a century or more.

[1] LONG, *op. cit.*

# ( 4 )
# BOARD
## wooden boxes and cardboard boxes

THE CARDBOARD BOX or packet is probably the first thing we think of when packaging is mentioned, and certainly it is one of the most widely used forms of package – as it has been for a very long time. Tracing its history is unnecessarily difficult because of the different meanings given to the same words at different times and by different people: anyone who tries to make sense of contemporary records soon realizes that a boxmaker could be a worker in wood or in cardboard; the word 'board' could mean either of these materials; and 'chip' could mean a thin sliver of wood or chip*board*, which was (and is) a kind of cardboard. Even the word 'cardboard' itself has not the clear meaning one might expect it to have: it is the familiar term in England, but in America 'paperboard' is more common, and in official English, including the title of the British Paper Box Federation, 'paper' sometimes means cardboard.

Samuel Pepys was presumably using the word in this sense when, on 24 October 1660, he took occasion to be angry with his wife 'about her putting up of half a crowne of mine in a paper box, which she had forgot where she had lain it'. We shall never know just what kind of box this was: in three editions of Pepys' *Diary*, the three learned editors have omitted to explain the phrase, unusual though it must have been at the time it was written.

The existence of inexpensive boxes was taken for granted in at least one trade before the end of Samuel Pepys' century: this we learn from an advertisement of 1696 for 'Excellent purging Pills prepared by *John Pechey . . . Basing-Lane, London.* The price of each Box is one Shilling Sixpence with directions for use'.[1]

We cannot say, today, what those early pillboxes were made of, but there is evidence to suggest that the first small, cheap, simple boxes were of scaleboard (*i.e.* wooden); in an English patent application of 1635 Sarah Jerome and William Webb sought patent protection for 'an engyne for the cutting of tymber in thynne peeces called scales for the makeing of band boxes and the like'. Fortunately, ambiguities between wood and cardboard in early references to box-making are not as important as they might seem because many boxmakers worked with both materials, and until well on in the nineteenth century the characteristics of both materials were hidden under paper labels or all-over paper wrappers. Neither wood nor the early box-board was a suitable surface for printing, and the graphic design was printed on paper to be pasted on.

[1] Quoted by Drummond and Wilbraham in *The Englishman's Food*.

# MATERIALS

Cardboard boxes were seldom handsome enough to be worth saving for their own sake like pot lids, or strong enough to be kept for re-use like tea tins or biscuit tins, and as a result early examples are hard to find. Something that looks very like a cardboard box full of books appears in an engraving of a London bookshop *c.* 1793, but the oldest box actually in existence which can be regarded as commercial packaging is a wooden one, The Infant's Cabinet of Fishes, 1801 (plate 74). As the name may suggest, this contains a set of picture cards for children. Its lid is paper-labelled and the label is printed with the name of the contents, the manufacturer's name and address (John Marshall of Aldermary Church Yard, London), and an eye-catching picture of fishes in a bowl.

It is difficult, if not impossible, to separate the early history of packaging from the early history of boxmaking, but it is evident that some of the first boxmakers in England were craftsmen who made boxes to sell, empty, to the public, not to sell to manufacturers for the packaging of their products: in this category were the widow Cooper, already mentioned (page 31), and the street vendor of 'Band Boxes' who was the subject of a plate in *Modern London,* 1805, which showed him crying his wares in Bond Street (plate 73).

The first serious research into early boxmaking in Britain was undertaken by the anonymous author of a series of articles published in a now defunct trade journal, the *Paper Container,* in 1922. He dates the birth of the boxmaking industry in Britain as 1817, the year in which the oldest boxmaking business known by name was established – M. Treverton & Son. A firm of this name was still trading 105 years later, when the *Paper Container* articles appeared;[1] it had been founded when a Mr Treverton 'placed on the market in London a small box which was made of chipwood and covered both inside and out with paper, the whole thing being something similar to our present matchbox'. Treverton seems to have got the idea – which was scarcely a revolutionary one, even in 1817 – from a Frenchman with whom he was associated, whose name has not come down to us.

London's second recorded boxmaker was William Austin, who used paper tubes made from old ledger paper to make round boxes of the pill-box type; presumably by this use of second-hand material he was able to price them even lower than chipwood boxes of the same shape. It is thought that Austin took over the business (in 1825) from a manufacturer who was also a street vendor of boxes.

Later, his son, James Austin, set out for America but only got as far as Liverpool, where he established the city's first boxmaking business in 1850. He was still there in 1892, and still held 'the only medal awarded (a bronze one) for paper boxes at the Great Exhibition of 1851'. The Liverpool business long continued as a family concern: James Austin died in the spring of 1897 but his son and daughter carried on the firm, and it became a limited company under the son, another William, in 1912.

To turn back for a moment to the earliest years of the boxmaking trade in the capital:

[1] In the 1922 *Post Office Directory* M. Treverton & Son appeared as 'plain and fancy box makers for chemists, confectioners, drapers, tie makers, stationers & jewellers; drapers' fixture boxes (established 1817) 33 Spittal Sq [Bishopsgate]'. By 1926 they had vanished completely from the London scene, or at least from the *Directory.*

Pigot & Co's *London Commercial Directory* for 1823–4 does not list any of the names mentioned in the *Paper Container* but has a section for pill-box makers with six different names in it – Bice, Coombs, Ford, Jones, Shearman, Shermur. Perhaps significantly, the only other entries in this directory concerned in any way with boxmaking appear under the heading of 'MISCELLANEOUS and names that came too late. . . .' They are: Richard Williams, scaleboard cutter; Robert Fitch, hat-box maker; and Bishop, of Parker Street, Drury Lane, who described himself unequivocally as a 'paper and chip box manufacturer'.

In Manchester in 1859 Hugh Stevenson bought a boxmaking business which had been established some time earlier by a Mr Cronheim. Stevenson's descendants' records show that he had about twenty employees when he started, and 100 by 1877.

In Treverton's time there is some record of a Frenchman being in business as a manufacturer of paper boxes in Manchester, according to the *Paper Container*; but I can find no reference to boxmaking in Manchester commercial directories of 1816–17. In most English provincial towns, indeed, the trade did not develop till some years later. John Walker, a Stockton-on-Tees chemist, invented matches and put them on the market in 1826–7; and he had to go to a local bookbinder, John Ellis, to make pasteboard boxes for them. It is likely that the same kind of thing happened in other towns too, for bookbinders – as has already been noted, page 53 – were versatile people, and pulpboard had been manufactured for book covers long before it was manufactured for boxes.

Perhaps the oldest cardboard package still to be seen is a box in the Victoria & Albert Museum attributed to the first quarter of the nineteenth century and made in Germany for 'The game of besieging'; the oldest *with a date on it* – 1834 – is English: the lid of a Mechi's Magic Strop box.

We must at this point remind ourselves that the growing popularity of cardboard did not mean the end of small wooden boxes. Throughout the period with which this book is concerned (and beyond), wood has been used for the packaging of a variety of products – not only obvious ones like fruit, sweets, and cigars (plates 76–80 and 82) but garden seeds in America (plate 81) bottles of ink in England (plate C), and some of the earliest motorcar sparking plugs.

# America's first boxmakers

IN AMERICA, early boxmaking followed a similar course – except that it did not begin in the capital. According to Edwin J. Schoettle, 'Philadelphia was the birthplace of paperboard boxes in the United States . . . prior to 1810. The birth dates from the time of migration of a large number of hand-knitters from Nottingham. . . . The first paperboard boxes in the United States were made at Philadelphia to contain the work of the hand-knitters'. It is a fact that there were 150 stocking-frames, such as Nottinghamshire knitters used, in the Germantown and Philadelphia area in 1775, rising to 200 in 1815, but no first-hand evidence of the boxes remains.

Philadelphia directories[1] record that there were six box manufacturers in that city by 1800 –

---

[1] Quoted by H. J. Bettendorf: see bibliography.

the first, Frederick Newman, being mentioned as early as 1785. But the oldest American box which can be associated with a specific manufactured product probably dates from the early years of the nineteenth century; for Ward & Co's Patent Persian Thread.

To replace imports into America from Britain and Germany 'the first commercial boxes of the set-up box type, for the jewelry trade'[1] were made by Aaron Lufkin Dennison, a Boston watchmaker and jeweller, in 1839. Five years later – reversing the usual sequence of events in family businesses – Aaron handed over the boxmaking side of his enterprise to his father, Colonel Andrew Dennison.

Andrew's own shoe business had fallen on hard times, and his son saw an opportunity to make good use of the father's craftsmanship in cutting out paper forms which two sisters living at home (in Brunswick, Maine) could make up into jewellers' boxes. These found a market in Boston, and soon the Dennison family was making a living, though not a fortune, from its efforts: in 1855 Colonel Dennison sold out (for $9000) to another son with even more memorable names than Aaron Lufkin's – Eliphalet Whorf Dennison. The family's main technical achievement was the development of equipment for creasing and cutting the box-board mechanically, whereas before it had to be shaped by hand round a wooden former or mandrel. From this time onwards, boxmaking by hand was old-fashioned though by no means obsolete.

PERHAPS the difficulty of making clean creases and sharp corners explains why so many nineteenth-century boxes were either round or oval, whether they were to contain Superior German Floating Lights, percussion caps, plate powder (page 35), nipple shields, hats (plate 89), chocolates (plates 93 to 95) or fruit. As early as 1817 Fortnum & Mason were advertising Portugal plums 'in the usual round boxes'; these were probably of wood chip, like the box for Vine Valley grapes (plate 76) which is now in the American Museum in Britain. Eighty years later, American boxmakers were producing round boxes in vast quantities for cylindrical phonograph records; in this instance the shape of the package was no doubt determined by the shape of the product. Because of the wide interest in early sound-recording equipment, many of these packs, for Edison and other makes of record (plate 90), still exist in private ownership and in public collections including the Herbert Museum, Coventry, and the Cuming Museum, Southwark. Some are wholly of pulpboard, some have let-in wooden bases.

But the product which, above all, one regards as a 'natural' for packaging in round boxes is the pill. By the 1890s Beechams of St Helens, Lancashire, claimed that they were selling 6,000,000 boxes of pills a year; and long before that, Robinson's of Chesterfield, one of the few boxmaking concerns whose history has been recorded for more than a century, had started in business as pill-box manufacturers. It was in 1839 that John Bradbury Robinson turned his back on 21 years of life as a chemist and druggist, and started a new career by taking over a pill-box business established even earlier by a Mr Fletcher.[2]

[1] Bettendorf, *op. cit.*

[2] Not until 1846 did Robinson begin to make square boxes, of wood chip: to run this new branch of the business, he brought a Mr Treverton from London. The name is sufficiently unusual to suggest that he was a member of the Treverton family which had established a pioneer boxmaking business nearly 30 years earlier; unfortunately there is nothing in Robinsons' records to confirm this or contradict it.

C

Wooden travelling pack and bottle for H. C. Stephens' Blue Black Writing Ink for Fountain Pens
Mineral-water bottle with marble-in-the-neck stopper for C. M. Ballinger, Monmouth, by Powell, Bristol
Embossed and printed tin for Farrah's toffee. Design registered 1890, in use 1967
Metal box for Bryant & May's Royal Wax Vestas, in the form of a letter-box. Early 20th century
Wooden box with sliding lid, spatter-painted and labelled, for Ladies' Pens by William Palmer, Royal
Pen Manufactory, East Grinstead, 'PEN CUTTER to the ROYAL FAMILY' c. 1850
Paper-labelled pot for Parisian Polish by E. Brown & Son. After 1862
Plaid-paper-covered box for vestas. Metal matchbox, embossed 'BRYANT & MAY. LIMITED'
Oval tin for Savoury Meat Lozenges by Brand & Co Ltd, London, Purveyors to H.M. King Edward VII
Rowntree's chocolate tin, commemorating the coronation of King Edward VII and Queen Alexandra

Similar round boxes were made in the United States and, from 1882, in Canada: Lawson & Jones of London, Ontario, was established in that year as a druggist box and label house. Canadian production methods were much the same as British; the boxes were hand-made, the blanks being die-cut and then banded into shape with strips of cover paper cut to size and made sticky with paste.[1] At least one brand of licorice in France was being packaged in boxes of a similar kind in 1966 (plate 83).

Large box used as a 'display outer' for smaller individual packages; advertised in an early issue of the *Chemist & Druggist* (established 1859)

Small round boxes covered in plaid paper had an exceptionally long run of popularity in Australia; at first (from about 1865) they were imported as matchboxes from Britain, and from 1896, when R. Bell & Co of London started making matches in Australia, they were made locally. It was not their original contents that earned them a place in Australian history, however, but their adaptability to other and more valuable contents long after the matches were spent. Because of their convenient size and snug-fitting lids, the gold miners used them as containers first for gold dust and later for gold sovereigns: the boxes were not only the right shape but the right size for sovereigns stacked one on another. Many of these plaid-paper-covered matchboxes were of cardboard, a few of wood or tinplate. Their popularity, which began with the gold rush, outlasted it by many years: they were still being made in Australia up to 1950.

IN THE 1850s and '60s it was the practice of some English chocolate manufacturers to buy sheets of pictures for their box-tops from printers on the Continent and from the few in England who specialized in colour printing. This was a way of decorating boxes, certainly; but it did not make them immediately identifiable as containing the products of a certain firm – which was becoming more desirable as competition between manufacturers was increasing.

Cadburys solved the problem by designing their own boxtops. One of the partners at this time was Richard Cadbury, the second son of the founder, who had joined the firm in 1850, at the age of fifteen, and proved to be a man of some artistic ability besides maintaining the Birmingham reputation for astuteness. He first painted the pictures he wanted, then found printers who could reproduce them in sheets in full colour at economic prices: no mean feat at the time. Today his paintings (plate 94) seem amateurish, but, in the words of Iolo Williams, 'the idea was fresh to the public then, and the box-lids . . . attracted a good deal of attention, and were the subject of a certain number of press paragraphs'. (*The Firm of Cadbury 1831–1931*).

By the 1900s, some fantastically elaborate chocolate boxes were being made – hand-made –

[1] Information given by C. R. Rowntree, president, Lawson & Jones Ltd, in a letter, November 1954.

especially for the Christmas-present season. Pleated silk and satin, heavy metal clasps, and hand-painted designs were the fashion; this was casket-making rather than packaging. Frys, like Cadburys, sold many of their best chocolates in fancy boxes made in their own works, and in 1908 a whole room in their Bristol factory was devoted to gold- and silver-blocking – its atmosphere no doubt richly laden with gold and silver dust.

# Fathers of the folding box

AS SOON as firms began to use boxes in really large quantities, it must have become evident that much space was wasted on their premises when they had to store empty made-up boxes. The obvious solution was to make folding boxes and supply them flat, so that the firm using them need not make them up until they were wanted, and could stack them in the smallest possible space meanwhile.

According to Bettendorf, the first folding cartons were made in America in 1850, or possibly even earlier, for Bird & Son's carpet tacks. These cartons were literally made up at the last moment – shaped round a wooden former by the store clerk at the point of sale – and produced in quarter-pound, half-pound, and one-pound sizes.

In the 1870s, Robert Gair, not content with the growth of his trade in paper bags, was taking a close interest in folding cartons for many commodities. The necessary creasing of the board was done on a platen press from which the inking mechanism had been removed; but from this stage to completion several tedious hand processes were involved. Gair wanted to do better than this, and before long he did. In April 1879, a machine-minder in his works, who was printing seed bags, carelessly allowed one of the metal rules to work-up so that where it touched the paper the bags were not merely imprinted but cut. 'The clean incisions struck the eye of Robert Gair at a moment when his mind was ready and receptive for the sight. It came to him, in a flash, that there was a way of constructing a multiple die that would cut and crease box-board in a single operation'.[1] The secret was to set the sharp cutting blades slightly higher than the blunt blades which would make the creases.

So the machine-made folding box or carton was invented: Gair lost no time in adapting a second-hand press, which he bought for $30, to cut and crease 750 sheets an hour, with ten carton blanks to the sheet. An output of 7,500 cartons an hour from one machine was bound to put Robert Gair ahead of his rivals, and to protect his position he went to Washington in person to file a patent application. It was suggested to him that some phrases in the specification needed revision, but Gair would not agree to this and as a result his application was turned down: three years later the first folding-box patent was granted to another firm. Long afterwards, he rescued his original press from a scrap-heap, put it on show in the entrance to his factory, and labelled it uncompromisingly: THE FATHER OF THE FOLDING BOX.

IF NEWS of Gair's invention reached England quickly, it did not rouse any wild enthusiasm here. Late in 1887, the year of Victoria's golden jubilee, a New York milliner called Isaac Watts

1 Allen Smith: see bibliography.

Parmenter set out for Europe with the sole selling rights in Colt cutting and creasing presses, but he found so little interest that he decided to start his own boxmaking business in London as well. His first order was for 100,000 cartons for Murray's 'American' Caramels, with the design printed on a wrapped-round paper label – a sizeable order at any time, especially so for the first folding-box order in Britain.

Other American interests soon followed Parmenter on the English boxmaking scene: the National Folding Box & Paper Co of New Haven appointed Samuel Cropper as its London 'correspondent' or agent, and competition between the two was keen. At one time, Parmenter's company changed its name to The National Folding Box Co Ltd. This understandably annoyed Cropper's American principals, and in 1894 he brought an action against Parmenter, who was forced to submit to an injunction never to use the National name again. Instead, he changed the name of his company to Britannia Folding Box Co Ltd: and this name has continued to the present day.

Bonbon carton by the Britannia Folding Box Co Ltd, London, 1897; 'theatre' chocolate box and cigarette carton by the same firm, 1896. The carton held two layers of six cigarettes each: at this time Players also packed cigarettes in twelves, not tens

The market for cartons was big enough to provide *lebensraum* for these companies (plates 101, 103 and 108–109) and for many others. Established boxmakers eventually saw the advantages of folding boxes and installed the necessary machinery to make them. Robinsons of Bristol worked in close contact with Gair's firm in New York; Tillotsons of Bolton began carton-making in 1897 with Robert Gair and John Thompson (Colt) presses from America. In the same decade J. B. Robinson & Son of Chesterfield were using machines of German design with which each crease was made separately; the cardboard blank was handled six times for creasing and twice for punching. Robinsons were not the only British boxmakers to install German equipment – but some others' German machines worked faster than theirs, if contemporary advertising is to be believed (plate 115).

There were over 800 patents relating to folding boxes by 1897, when the *Box-maker's Journal* summed-up the difference between American and German methods in this way: 'the method of making folding boxes by grooving and stamping . . . originated in Germany, but we are indebted to the Americans for the newer process of creasing'. German machinery was widely used in making the heavier types of folding box which were sent out flat from the box-makers and required wire-stitching for their setting-up on the user firm's premises. The firm of Burgon & Co was established in Manchester in 1869 to make such boxes: in 1954, **Mr B. Camp-bell**, grandson of the founder William Burgon, recalled the days more than fifty years earlier when, as one of his first jobs in the family business, he bought stitching machines from Germany at £10 each, to sell to customers at about £16 10s. The customers included dyers and cleaners in Liverpool and slipper manufacturers in the Rossendale valley; Burgons' suppliers of 'granite board' were the Thames Paper Co, already mentioned (p. 29).

THE 'NINETIES were also the decade which saw the birth of one of the most prolific of all forms of folding box – the cigarette carton. Originally known as 'sliding cases', these cartons were first used in 1892 for Wills's Three Castles cigarettes, and by 1894 for several other Wills brands[1] (plate 97). They must have been made by hand, for it was not until 1898 that their manufacturers, Mardon Son & Hall, installed their first machine designed specially for making cigarette cartons – a Franklin, made in Philadelphia, with an output of a million cartons a week. This was probably the first of its kind in Britain, but round about the same time Tillotsons opened an additional factory in Bolton in which *three* American cigarette carton machines, known as Baron tubers, were installed. It was already evident that the cigarette habit was going to mean a lot of business for boxmakers on both sides of the Atlantic (plates 98–100 and 167).

By the early years of the twentieth century, the carton trade had developed many different forms of folding and shaping, with names that sound like extracts from a medieval torturer's vocabulary: shell and slide, heel and toe lock, band shape, claw lock and Colburn lock. The commodities now packaged in board included Elijah's Manna (whose exact nature has not been handed down to posterity) and a variety of less mysterious 'everyday things' that included candles (plate 118) and candy; gas mantles and Grape-Nuts (introduced in 1898); oats (plate 124) and wheatflakes; and the famous Uneeda biscuits (plate 125). Their pack was an unprinted paper-board carton lined with waxed paper on the inside and completely overwrapped with printed paper which carried quite a lot of wording besides the brand-name. This is said to have been suggested by Robert Gair's son who, when the biscuit makers told him of their plans for a new product which was to be nationally advertised, made the sensible comment, 'You need a name'. The name and the carton spelt the end of the cracker-barrel era in American storekeeping.

[1] The first (rigid) cardboard boxes for Wills's cigarettes had been made in 1883 by Mardon Son & Hall; these were for cigarettes in 100s.

Late nineteenth-century cartons for the Star Drug Co, London and New York

Typical folding box constructions of 1896 from the catalogue of the Britannia Folding Box Co.
*Below left*, egg box; *right, top to bottom*, drug tuck, Colburn lock and bandbox or band shape

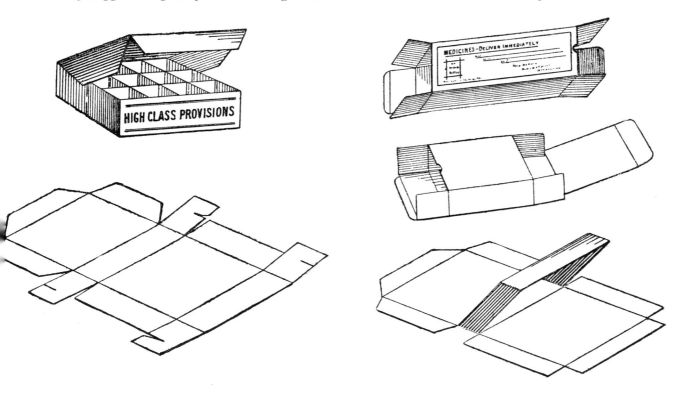

Group of tins for Victory Chlorodyne Lozenges, *c.* 1899

# (5)
# METAL
## boxes, cans,
## collapsible tubes

THE ANCIENT EGYPTIANS made metal boxes, but theirs were goldsmiths' wares – containers which may well have been more precious than the contents. The history of the metal box in packaging is shorter by many centuries: so far as available evidence shows, it begins in eighteenth-century London with a number of references to 'Canisters' in the ledgers, from 1764 onwards, of Fribourg & Treyer, the Haymarket tobacconists. These canisters contained snuff, and were charged to their customers at threepence, fourpence or sixpence according to size. The earliest metal pack is one of Fribourg & Treyer's, a small lead drum with a printed paper label round it, probably dating from the 1780s (plate 126).

To search for other uses of lead in the history of packaging, except in the form of lead foil, would be a dead-end occupation, for the predominant packaging metal was (and still is) tinplate. Nowadays, the word means steel coated with tin; earlier, it meant *iron* coated with tin – and tin-plate of this kind was made in Bohemia in the sixteenth century. In Britain it was produced commercially from the eighteenth century onwards, and used in packaging from the early nineteenth.

Among the first users of large metal drums (which they called 'cisterns') were varnish manu-facturers.[1] But the first individuals whose names appear in the story were the first maker of matches and a baker of biscuits: John Walker, of Stockton-on-Tees, already mentioned for his enterprise in getting cardboard matchboxes made locally, also packed his matches in round tins: there were a hundred matches to the tin, and they cost a halfpenny more in this pack than in a cardboard box.

The biscuit baker, Walker's contemporary, was Thomas Huntley, of Reading. In the early 1830s the stage coach was still the best method of travelling between London and Bath; the Crown Inn at Reading was one of the stages, and often, when a coach pulled in there, Huntley would send a boy from his shop a few yards away with a tray of cakes and biscuits for sale to the passengers. His biscuits were evidently good, for people remembered them afterwards and wrote for more. This presented a packaging problem: to solve it, Huntley called in the services of his brother Joseph, an ironmonger and tinsmith with premises only two doors from the Crown, who made him a supply of tin boxes in which the biscuits could safely be sent to customers in

---

[1] Especially after the 1840s, when they found the supply of stoneware jars inadequate in meeting the demand for coach varnish for Britain's growing railway system.

71

distant places. Thus Thomas Huntley and Joseph Huntley founded the fortunes of two businesses, Huntley & Palmers and Huntley, Boorne & Stevens, both still of Reading. (Palmer the engineer joined Huntley the baker in 1841.)

What the first biscuit tins looked like is unfortunately a matter for conjecture, as no illustration or description of them is known to exist. But we know that in Thomas Huntley's day there were already various ways of putting words or designs on to a metal box: the most permanent was embossing, which could be used for descriptive wording or even for designs with considerable small detail in them (plates 128–131). A method of decoration which could not be used to apply a design but gave the metal surface some textural interest was the crystallization or *moiré métallique* process, said to have been introduced from France early in the nineteenth century. This produced a surface rather similar to a modern galvanized or 'crackle' finish, and it had the practical advantage of helping to hide any small blemishes in the metal (plate 136).

The most common form of decoration for early metal boxes, as for early board boxes, was, however, a paper label. Paper printing was a well-tried process; most towns had printers, and labels were cheap. During the 1840s, Huntley & Palmer were using a pictorial label printed for them in London by De La Rue (plate 193) – a label illustrating their Biscuit Manufactory, and behind it one of the trains of the new railway (the Great Western, built between 1835 and 1841) which had almost put an end to stage-coach days at Reading, though not to the prosperity of Huntley & Palmers.

It was easy to stick paper labels (plate 157) or to solder thin metal labels (plate 127) on tins as some early canners did, both in England and France; but it was also easy for over-long storage or damp or rough handling to remove such labels. There were obvious advantages in printing names and designs on the tinplate itself if this could be done, and one of the most fascinating chapters in the whole history of packaging is concerned with the different ways in which the problem of tin-printing was tackled between the 1850s and the end of the century. This problem arose from the nature of a metal sheet: it does not absorb ink to 'take' the impression as paper or board does, and the contact between hard tinplate and hard type-metal or lithographic stones is bound to be unsympathetic.

Although there were many tin-printing patents in Britain, France and the United States, they can all be grouped under three broad headings – first direct printing on the tinplate; second transfer-printing; and last, in 1875, the process now known as offset lithography, which at first was also called 'direct' tin-printing.

The name that is most often associated with the original direct methods is that of the Tin Plate Decorating Co, established *c.* 1861–2 in Glamorganshire, South Wales. This private firm shared its premises, at Melincrythan on the outskirts of Neath, with a firm of tinplate manufacturers, Leach, Flower & Co; Philip William Flower and Wickham Flower were principals of both firms,[1] and the sheets printed by the Tin Plate Decorating Co were often marked FLOWERS PATENT. The Flowers were in fact concerned in at least two patents, both of which were described in patent-office terminology as 'communicated' from France: one of these patents, granted in 1864, sought to improve the quality of printing on tin by the use of lead-based inks; the other,

[1] Philip William Flower was also the author of a *History of the Trade in Tin*: see bibliography.

in 1869, covered the application of a coating of paint or alloy to the tinplate before printing on it.

But the problem of printing with two non-absorbent surfaces pressed against each other could not be satisfactorily solved, and before long the Tin Plate Decorating Co was using the transfer process – which entailed printing designs on thin transfer paper (plate 135) and applying the transfers to the tinplate, rather as the Battersea enamellers had done on their enamelled boxes a century earlier.

A pioneer of this process for metal box decoration was Benjamin George George of Hatton Garden: he was a book-printer also, and a prolific patentee,[1] and at the Great International Exhibition in London in 1862[2] he exhibited 'patent ornamental show tablets . . . for advertising purposes'. It is not certain that these were printed tablets, but if George was not tin-printing then, he certainly was doing so a few years later. We have the first-hand evidence of a Huntley & Palmers' biscuit tin, marked 'Ben. George, Patentee, London' (plate 134) and the documentary evidence of patents granted to him in 1870 and 1873 which show that he was already experienced in transfer-printing on tin.

At first it was customary for sheets of tinplate to be painted over in oil colour, dried, and rubbed down before the transfers were applied, and this sequence of operations might be re-peated several times according to the finish and polish required. Benjamin George's 1870 patent substituted extra coats of flat colour *printed* on the transfer paper – printed last, and so coming off first – for the coat of paint on the tinplate; this eliminated a tedious hand process. His 1873 patent went still further in speeding-up transfer printing by sandwiching the transfer papers and tinplate sheets between layers of cardboard and subjecting them to the pressure of a pair of re-volving rollers, so that 10, 20, or even 40 sheets (he claimed) could be printed at a time.

Transfer-printing was to remain in general use for another twenty years or more (plates 135 and 142), but in 1875 two patents introduced the process which eventually supplanted it – 'direct' tin-printing ('semi-direct' might have been a better name) by offset lithography. The first of these patents was awarded to Robert Barclay and John Doyle Fry, partners in the City printing house of Barclay & Fry, and was 'partly a communication from abroad by Henry Baber, of Paris'; the second was in the name of Robert Barclay only.

The process which the patents covered was successful because it avoided the use of trans-fers and at the same time avoided direct contact between lithographic stone and tinplate; the design from the stone was printed on a glazed cardboard blanket first, and immediately 'offset' from that on to the metal sheets. Barclay's second patent referred to 'the use of an impression cylinder receiving the impressions and transferring them by "set off" to the metal plates'.

Thus was invented the process still used for tin-printing and now used even more widely in

---

[1] His patents included no. 2434 of 1861, for 'pro-ducing embossed ornamentation'; 2463/1863, 'tab-lets . . . for advertising . . .'; 2690/1866, 'manufacture of show-cards'; 2333/1868, 'improved machinery for bronzing printed work'; 8/1869, 'manufacture of show cards and other ornamental surfaces'. His 1870 transfer-printing patent threw in for good measure the use of clear lacquers instead of bronze powder on

tinplate where a metallic sheen was required, and the use of tin-printing and embossing together to give extra richness to a design. London directories show that Ben George was in business in Hatton Garden from 1856 to 1893.

[2] Two other exhibitors at this exhibition claimed to display 'printing on metal' – Adams & Gee of Smithfield and Captain H. B. Coathupe of Kensington.

paper printing – a staple means of production for popular magazines, mail-order catalogues and other multi-coloured mass media. In its origins offset-litho was primarily a package-printing and wholly a tin-printing process; tin-printing has never been very widely used outside the metal box business, except for mechanical toys and the 'cheap tin trays' of John Masefield's *Cargoes*.

Robert Barclay may have had little idea of the potential value of the invention. He could not find the capital or the time to exploit it fully, and sold the exclusive rights in his patent to Bryant & May, of Bow, the match manufacturers. Their own interest was in the printing of metal covers for Vesta matchboxes, but they realized that 'direct' tin-printing could be of value to other industries, and licensed Huntley, Boorne & Stevens of Reading to print by Barclay's process. All the recorded facts[1] point in this direction but there was a strong oral tradition in the Reading firm that the patent rights which Bryant & May licensed to them had been acquired as part payment of a bad debt incurred in France. This *may* be so; the mysterious-Frenchman myth is even more persistent, and perhaps with more justification, in the tin-printing industry than in cardboard boxmaking: according to Turner Berry,[2] British tin-printers' transfers were imported from Paris, and the 'communication' of patents across the Channel is certainly a matter of fact. It may be that the Huntley, Boorne & Stevens tradition is an unconscious tribute to the involvement of Henry Baber of Paris in the first Barclay & Fry patent.

Yet another version of the beginnings of tin-printing was put forward by Lee Wright, of the old-established printing machinery firm of George Mann & Co Ltd, in a lecture in London in 1959:[2] he considered it likely that several inventors hit on the same idea about the same time and that a 'secret' offset-lithographic press was built for Huntley, Boorne & Stevens but not patented by Hopkinson & Cope of London, better known as manufacturers of Albion presses. A further development of the Barclay-patented process was necessary before it became commercially practicable: the substitution of a rubber-covered canvas sheet for glazed cardboard as the 'offsetting' medium. (Later, this was in turn to be superseded by a rubber-composition roller.)

Robert Barclay died suddenly and unexpectedly in 1877; his patent lapsed expectedly in 1889. So many people were so eager to use his process, once they were free to do so, that from this date onwards the days of metal-box decoration by the old transfer process were numbered.

---

[1] The archives of Barclay & Fry include this 'proposal to Messrs Bryant & May' dated 1 June 1875:

We will agree to instruct Messrs Huntley Boorne & Stevens of Reading as your representatives in a process which shall not infringe Flowers or Ben Georges patents for producing printed tin on metal plates. We will enable them to supply you as nearly as can be reckoned at a cost of one shilling 1s per 100 for printing on plates of the largest size printed in Black in a manner superior to Flower's plates . . . you can hardly fail to realize a considerable profit as large consumers during the continuance of Flowers & Ben Georges patents & from their present position of practical monopoly . . . we ask quite irrespectively of any question as to the validity of our letters patent when sealed to be adequately remunerated for our trouble. . . . We will sell the patent absolutely. . . . (reserving to ourselves the right to print Shew Cards & also the right to license one other House or print ourselves if the Royalty should not be payable on an average of 20,000 plates per week for 12 mts [months]).

The matter must have dragged on, for in November 1877 the assignment of patents had not, apparently, reached legal completion. In that month Fry wrote to R. Smith Esq, presumably one of the solicitors concerned:

I am obliged by your letter of today enclosing cheque, also copies of assignt & indemnity from Bryant & May. . . . I shall be glad to hear Ellis's opinion, that I may decide about the lease, so that assignt may be completed.

[2] See bibliography.

Label from a round tin for snuff, late nineteenth century

But for the wording one might assume that this varnish-tin label was far older than any 'motor body', but it followed the style of other labels already in use by Masons. (A motorcar was illustrated on a package in 1897 – a Peek Frean biscuit tin commemorating Queen Victoria's diamond jubilee)

Paper-labelled tin for Menier cocoa; early twentieth century

## MATERIALS

By the end of the Victorian era, there were several well-known metal boxmakers in Britain; they were also tin-printers, and what had started as two separate industries had virtually become one. Barclay & Fry Ltd opened a metal box works in Southwark in the 1890s. Another pioneer firm who moved in from printing was Hudson Scott of Carlisle: Barringers of Mansfield, on the other hand, were boxmakers who later became tin-printers.

Hudson Scott could trace their origins, in paper-printing, back to 1799. They began transfer-printing tin about 1876, and replaced this process by direct tin-printing when Barclay's patent lapsed: there is a story that they had bought machines on the Continent and run them in well *before* it lapsed, so that they could burst into the new business, with full confidence in their own ability, the moment the law allowed them to print by methods formerly forbidden to them. After

Advertisement illustration of a boot-polish tin, 1910

some years of supplying printed sheets to customers to make up into boxes, they opened a metal-box works of their own, installing tools for the manufacture of hinged-lid tins for tea, tobacco and Carr's biscuits. Their finest hour was yet to come: they made, embossed and printed most of the 100,000 tin boxes in which Queen Victoria sent chocolates to her soldiers serving in the South African war (plate 132). This brought Hudson Scott a royal warrant, and the tins enjoyed a lasting popularity; a considerable number were reported to be in existence in the early 1960s, some of them handed down through two generations with the chocolate still intact.

Barringers' story is more involved. Originally, Barringer & Brown were packers of various commodities including mustard; in the 1860s they were selling mustard in tins which were hand-made by their own workpeople and decorated either with printed paper labels or with transfer-printing by the Tin Plate Decorating Co. Occasionally both forms of decoration were used on the same tin (plate 133). One partner in the firm, Charles Manners, was especially interested in the metal-boxmaking side of their activities, and developed it so successfully that Barringers found themselves able to sell tins to other manufacturers. Soon they were transfer-printing tins both for their own mustard and for customers' products (plate 189); and in the 1890s a separate company, Barringer, Wallis & Manners Ltd, was formed to develop this trade. Later they were to win themselves a place in the annals of printing by installing the first rotary tin-printing press. All offset-litho tin-printing had been done on flatbed presses until, in 1903, the Mann Standard rotary was introduced; the first machine of this kind, awarded a special silver medal at the London Printing Exhibition of 1904, was installed at Barringer, Wallis & Manners' Rock Valley works.[1]

To step outside our historical sequence for a moment: several firms, including Barclay & Fry, Hudson Scott, and Barringer Wallis & Manners, were to combine to form Allied Tin Box Makers Ltd. That was in 1921; the new company changed its name to Metal Box & Printing Industries in the following year, and became the Metal Box Co Ltd, a public company with £2,000,000 capital, in 1930. Barringers' fate was a good deal happier than that of their old suppliers, the Tin Plate Decorating Co: this became a limited company in 1885, found itself in the hands of a receiver and manager in 1910, and was finally wound-up on 21 November 1912. (To confuse the historian, however, another company was formed immediately afterwards, with the same name, at the same works at Melincrythan.)

# American metal boxes

The story of the metal box in Britain is fragmentary; in America the fragments are even fewer and farther apart. Probably the earliest American metal boxes in existence today are gunpowder flasks[2] now in the possession of the New York Historical Society; the next earliest, a tomato can. This can is notable for having one of the first coloured labels (plate 158). The colours – green for leaves and brownish-red for fruit – were used to depict a dish of tomatoes, in a style which suggests a date in the 1860s.

The first known *printed* metal box in America was a seamless oval tin to hold a cake of solidified toothpowder made by Dr Israel Whitney Lyon, a dentist whose calling had taken him to California in the gold-rush days, and later into the Civil War, before he began his manufacturing business some time in 1866 – late in 1866 one hopes, because he sold only $211 worth of his 'cakes' in that year. The date makes it probable that his tins were transfer-printed (plate 146).

Ten years later – a year after Robert Barclay in Britain discovered offset-litho as the solution to the problem of how to print 'direct' on tin – American inventors were still seeking other solutions. U.S. patent no. 172,894, dated 1 February 1876, was granted to Legrand B. Smith of New York for 'Improvements in Ornamenting Metal'. Smith's object was familiar: 'the production

---

[1] George Mann & Co of Leeds had already marketed a successful flatbed tin-printing press, the Improved Climax, which they sold in some numbers, at £300. It had been patented in 1892 by Mann's partner, Charles Pollard, and could be adapted – for £8 extra - for litho-printing on paper.

[2] Paper-labelled: illustrated in *Printed Ephemera* by John Lewis. The same circular engraved label was also used on the ends of small wooden casks; there is an example in the American Museum in Britain. Both types of pack were used for Kentucky Rifle Gunpowder, which was made at Hazardville near Enfield, Connecticut, by the Hazard Powder Company – established in 1843 by Augustus George Hazard (1802–1868).

of a metallic sheet with an imprint directly upon it of any desired figure or word, in as fine lines and delicate tints, or in a combination or multiplication of same, as can be produced upon paper or other similar fabric'; the discovery for which he obtained patent protection was a new one – and one which Ben George, among others, would have been unlikely to accept – that evenly roughened metal would pick up a printed image more readily than a perfectly smooth sheet, whether the roughening was done 'by the well-known sand-blast or other appropriate means'. A few months later, Smith was granted a further patent (182,336, of 17 October 1876) for making printed metal sheets resistant to alcohol, acids, and other liquids by doctoring the ink and heating the sheets sufficiently 'to effect a mechanical union or amalgamation of the print and the metal corrugations'. This heating process would only work satisfactorily with his roughened sheets, which allowed 'the foreign substances used in producing the designs to sink, in part, below the plane of the surface of the metal'; he claimed that with these sheets it would render the printed design permanent even on such things as beef cans, which had to be immersed for hours in boiling water. Unfortunately we do not know how successful Smith's methods were.

In 1887 the *American Lithographer & Printer* was recommending a reader to use a similar tin-printing technique to Barclay's. PRINTER had asked despairingly: 'Could you give me something practical on tin printing. I have tried three and four colors as directions call for in your paper, but the ink gets so hard that it will not lift the next color. I have seen some very fine work done with black on a red ground, and I have tried all I know of. . . .' The editorial ANSWER was: 'The best printing on tin is done as follows: The impression is at first made from the stone onto a rubber roller and from this roller the ink is rolled or transferred off again upon the tinplate. There has lately been invented a steampress, which we think has also been patented. This press is working in the same plan and the main principle is that, the rubber has the qualification of taking a much sharper impression than any kind of paper in the market, and by its elasticity has also the nature of printing smooth and solid on a hard surface, even if the same is uneven. If the ink becomes to [sic] hard, as you say, . . . add to the first colors you print a trifle of yellow wax with Venecian turpentine. This will prevent the trouble and the ink will lift readily'.

It is interesting to guess how many tin-printers there were in America at this time. Fuchs & Lang of New York found it worth while to advertise tin-printers' inks in 1888, but in that year the first *Lithographers' Directory* contained only three names under the heading of 'Printers (Tin)'. One – looking slightly misplaced – was Julius Klinkhardt of Leipzig, Saxony; another was A. Sachse & Co of Baltimore, Maryland; the third was given as Sohmer Bros of Brooklyn, New York, under this heading, but appeared as 'Somers Bros' under another heading ('Show Cards – Iron') in the same book.

The Somers brothers, Daniel, Joe and Guy, had started a metalworking business in Brooklyn in 1869, and were groping their way towards a practical tin-printing process: they had found one by 1879. All that is now known of it is that the process was lithographic (plate 148); that printing of the sheets was followed by lacquering: and that these stages, with the making-up of the boxes which they logically led to, took several days. In the next decade a patent for a machine 'for seaming irregular-shaped cans' was granted to William H. Atkinson, at Somers' address, who assigned it to the firm – presumably he was an employee; and later Daniel Somers himself ob-

D

Embossed metal box for Cough Cherries. The wording is printed on a separate sliding panel
Printed tin for Edgeworth tobacco by Larus & Bro. Co, Richmond, Virginia. American Can Co 1913
Rigid cardboard boxes with paper-labelled lids for Elmwood collars, patented 1871, from Davis & Boynton,
Tilton, N.H.; and for a game, Peter Coddle; McLoughlin Bros, New York, 1889
An early example of the seamless metal box: for Schenck's Mandrake Liver Pills, Philadelphia
Mathewsons Imperial Gun Powder tin: the label lithographed by B. W. Thayer & Co, Boston
Two-ounce tin by The Hasker & Marcuse Mfg. Co, Richmond, Virginia, for Lucky Strike cut plug by
R. A. Patterson Tobacco Co, also of Richmond. Before 1912

tained patent protection for 'a combined packing-box and show-stand composed of a plurality of reversible sections of different sizes' – sections nesting to form a box or extending to form a stand.

About 1883, Dr Lyon became a customer of Somers Bros: by this time he had abandoned his cakes of tooth powder in favour of loose powder, which he sold at first in green glass bottles but later in a new lithographed screw-capped round tin which Somers Bros had patented. In 1890, a somewhat similar tin was demanded from Somers by another of the founding fathers of American brand-names, a young chemist, Gerhard Mennen of Newark, New Jersey. Mennen had recently and successfully launched his baby powder in a pasteboard drum, but he had soon realized that a tin was likely to be more leakproof, and a sprinkler top could be fitted which would allow a half-turn for opening and closing. There was to be a removable cap over the sprinkler, and the design printed on the tinplate was to be a pattern of orange sunbursts against a dark blue background. But before this design got into print, two changes were made, as Alfred Lief was later to record in *The Mennen Story* : first, Mennen decided that his portrait on the pack would inspire confidence among American mothers; second, a jubilant salesman came into the shop with a photograph of his new baby and urged Mennen to use it. Mennen did. Both characters were to remain part of the American scene for many years: Gerhard was undoubtedly pleased but perhaps not greatly surprised when a mother in Akron, Ohio, wrote: 'My Florence is so grateful that she kisses the picture of the gentleman on the lid all day long' (plate 151).

In the back room behind Mennen's drugstore, the tins of talcum powder were filled by hand with a scoop and weighed on a small scale before the caps were fitted. Sometimes Mrs Mennen came in to help; and the business grew. Mennen went out with a minstrel party, Mennen's Talcum Show, and formed a company, Gerhard Mennen Chemical Co; and the business went on growing. Attention to packaging also helped its growth. A still more leakproof powder tin was devised by George F. Miller, plant manager at Somers Bros' factory, with a double seam and a better sprinkler top: and a new type of filling machine was devised to fill the tins from the bottom before the final seaming operation. (Regrettably, this machine meant the end of the domestic-industrial scene in the back room.) By 1900 Mennen had reached the comparative sophistication of 'The Box That Lox. . . .' In that year he advertised in the *Saturday Evening Post* for the first time: two years later he was dead – at the age of 45. His widow and eighteen-year-old son were to run the business with great success, taking over where the founder had left off.

Other American businesses, too, were growing – and using metal boxes (plates 147, 149–50, 154). In 1900, Taite & Sisler of Philadelphia, later to become the Clarke Can Co, was manufacturing 5,000 tooth-powder tins a day: and when the American Can Co was incorporated in New Jersey a year later, it combined *sixty* metal-box manufacturers. Presumably in America then, as in England a few years earlier, not all of these boxmakers were tin-printers.

It would be quite wrong to assume, because printing on tin was a technical triumph, that tin-printed boxes were ever the most common form of metal pack, either in America or in Britain. We can comparatively easily find examples of nineteenth-century printed tins because their usefulness as domestic containers ensured a long life for them after the original contents had been used, and they are such splendidly unselfconscious Victoriana that few people would have had the heart to throw out any which survived into recent years. But when printed tins appeared in the shops, they were packages *de luxe*, seen mainly as gift packs at Christmas and on other special occasions; for most metal-boxed commodities, a paper-labelled tin was the standard form of package. There is a clear reminder of this in Lewis Carroll's rather donnish reply to a suggestion, in 1891, that some of the *Looking Glass* illustrations should decorate a biscuit tin: 'The biscuit boxes I buy are covered with paper, which of course *might* be decorated with pictures, but I think it would be degrading Art to do so, as they would necessarily be torn to pieces in opening the box.' At this time most British biscuit manufacturers sent their products out to the grocers in large almost cube-shaped tins from which the biscuits were usually weighed out into paper bags – unless you were a big enough customer to buy nine or ten or fourteen pounds of biscuits at a time, the usual contents of the square tins (plates A & 206).

# Food canning

There is one form of metal container which, because of its social importance, deserves to be discussed separately: the food can, without which none of the jokes about tin-openers as the essential weapon in the housewife's armoury could ever have existed.

The first satisfactory method of food preservation in containers was evolved in France early in the nineteenth century, to feed Napoleon's armies. The history of canning, so called, from its invention by Nicolas Appert in 1809–10 has often been related; but it is not always realized that Appert at first used wide-necked glass jars sealed with laminated corks – not cans in the modern sense. These came later in his experiments, after he had spent some time in Britain and seen what was done here. Tinplate was first recommended for preserved-food containers (along with glass, pottery, and other 'fit materials') in a British patent, no. 3372 of 1810, granted to Peter Durand: he had apparently been in communication with Appert, and designed a cylindrical tin canister with a disc to be soldered over the small hole through which it was filled.

Between 1814 and 1830 Appert had his own can-making workshop and bought tinplate from two factories (at Bains and La Chaudeau), but he still favoured glass jars for domestic food packs, and regarded metal cans as only necessary in the arduous conditions of storage aboard ship.

In Britain, food canning as an industry began with Bryan Donkin and John Hall, who bought Durand's patent for £1,000 and set up the first canning factory in Blue Anchor Road, Bermondsey; they produced for the Admiralty supplies of 'patent preserved meats' or, as Sir Joseph Banks, the president of the Royal Society, called them, 'embalmed provisions' (1813–14). Donkin's successors, John Gamble & Company, supplied the Admiralty with canned food regularly from 1819 onwards, and some of the oldest food cans still surviving (plates 127 and 157) owe their existence to this firm (which was later merged with Crosse & Blackwell). A can of their Roasted Veal was taken on Parry's voyage in search of the North-West Passage in 1824, brought back, taken out again in 1826, and brought home a second time. Its body was made from a single piece of tinplate bent into a cylinder, with the edges folded together in a lock seam; a lifting-ring was soldered on top, and a paper label was stuck on. The label was printed with directions beginning: *Cut round on the top near to the outer edge with a chisel and hammer*... which serves as a reminder that the can was invented before the can-opener. (This doyen of all known food packs lay for many years in the Royal United Service Institution Museum, London. It was opened in 1936, when the contents were still good and were fed to animals without any ill effects.)

Soon after the English canners had got into their stride, canning industries sprang up elsewhere; in Scotland in the 1820s, for various kinds of fish; in France in the same decade, for sardines in oil. In Germany, plumbers, skilled in metalwork, took up canning as a sideline; in America, the first canners, Kensett and Underwood, were immigrants from England who clung to the idea of 'canning' in glass bottles after the English industry had established itself on the basis of tinplate cans.

Thomas Kensett had settled in America in 1812 and was an engraver of labels for food products. In 1819 he set up a small canning plant on the New York waterfront, where he canned oysters, meat and vegetables. A patent for preserving food in 'vessels of tin' was awarded to Kensett and his father-in-law, Ezra Daggett, in 1825. (Peter Durand had repeated *his* British patent in the United States in 1818.)

William Underwood emigrated to America in 1817 and began canning fruits and pickles at Boston, Mass., in 1819 – again, in bottles. Not until 1837 did he or Kensett change over completely from glass to tinplate, and it was a year or two after this before tin cans came into wide use in the United States.

There is little or no evidence of what the first cans or their labels looked like. The earliest known American can, already mentioned (plate 158), was painted sky-blue and its label was decorated with a steel engraving of tomatoes. Wording on the label makes it evident that canned food still needed to be explained to the potential customer: 'FRESH TOMATOES. . . . This valuable article is prepared ready for the table and fit for use with the exception of a little seasoning as suits the taste. If to be used warm, the case must be put into hot water fifteen minutes before opening. . . .'

LIKE TENNYSON'S view of freedom, and perhaps with more lasting results, the scope of food canning broadened down from precedent to precedent as the nineteenth century advanced: powdered milk was canned in Russia in 1842–3; salmon in Ireland in 1849; condensed milk in Britain in 1850, America in 1853 (Gail Borden's – patented in 1856), Switzerland in 1866. The Anglo-Swiss Condensed Milk Company was to become better known in later years with Nestlé: its Milk-Maid Brand took first prize at the Universal Exhibition in Paris in 1867 (page 82). Australia found a place on the canning map in 1846 when Sizar Elliot, an English immigrant, displayed the first Australian tinned meat at an exhibition in Sydney. (He saved some of the tins for 20 years and then exhibited again to show how well the meat had kept: well enough to earn him a medallion.) Elliot does not seem to have carried his canning far beyond the experimental stage, but the success of his experiments caused two other Australians to open meat canning factories within two years of the 1846 exhibition: M. Joseph at Camperdown, Sydney, and Henry Dangar at Newcastle. The latter cannery (later Henry & William Dangar's) continued in business for many years: about 1866, the Dangars began to export boiled mutton to England. The demand for this was limited, but later they were more successful with canned beef, which sold at about half the price of fresh meat from the butcher's. It was price rather than package design that established a market for Australian meat: a contemporary English observer (1874) described its containers as 'big, thick, clumsy red tins'.[1]

JULY 8, 1871.　　　THE GROCER.

**ANGLO-SWISS  CONDENSED  MILK  COMPANY,**

PURE.　　MILK-MAID BRAND.　　TRADE MARK.　　CONVENIENT.
DELICIOUS.　　　　　　　　　　　　　　　NO WASTE.
WHOLESOME.　　　　　　　　　　　　　　THE "ORIGINAL."
UNIFORM.　　　　　　　　　　　　　　THE CHEAPEST.
ECONOMICAL.　　　　　　　　　　　　　THE BEST.

**CONDENSED  MILK,**
"MILK-MAID BRAND."
ANGLO-SWISS CONDENSED MILK COMPANY, CHAM SWITZERLAND
AND
38, LEADENHALL-STREET, LONDON, E.C.
·FOUR MEDALS.·
PARIS, 1867.　|　HAVRE, 1868.　|　ALTONA, 1869.　|　CASSEL, 1870.
All First Prizes, obtained in competition with 3 to 8 other brands of Condensed Milk.
*Recommended by Baron Liebig, by "The Lancet," "The British Medical Journal," "The Food Journal," "The Milk Journal;"*
*approved by the Food Committee of the Society of Arts; adopted by Her Majesty's Emigration Commissioners,*
*and the Admiralty.*

Advertisement for one of the first brands of canned condensed milk. A later poster for the same brand can be seen in plate 207. By 1913 the combined Anglo-Swiss and Nestlé company controlled 22 canning plants between Norway and Australia

IT IS WELL KNOWN that Chicago, Hog Butcher for the World, developed a vast meat-packing industry in the second half of the nineteenth century, and one could easily be misled into thinking this was meat packaging in the twentieth-century meaning of the term, but at first the Chicago packers packed their meat in bulk, in wooden barrels. The unit pack, of convenient size for the housewife to open and the family to eat, probably began with Libby, McNeill & Libby in the early 'seventies (plate 160). In 1875 there was a great deal of controversy between Libbys and another Chicago packer, J. A. Wilson, as to who had originated the tapered shape of can which was typical of corned beef packaging then as it long continued to be. Eventually, after litigation, Libbys decided to drop a patent application which they had apparently been rather late in lodging, Wilson was awarded the patent – and his firm was bought up by Libbys.

Was it any truer then than now that a slight tap on the smaller end of a corned beef tin 'will cause the solidly packaged meat to slide out in one piece so as to be readily sliced'? This was Wilson's claim in U.S. Patent 161,848 of 12 October 1878. The convenience of the consumer was certainly studied; moreover, the compressed meat showed such a saving in bulk over meat packed in the old way, in barrels, that it was a more readily exportable commodity – and exported it was, in vast quantities from the late 1870s onwards, from the New World to the Old.

The technical advances in a century of food canning are too numerous to be listed here, but space must be found for a warning which was considered necessary, in spite of technical pro-

[1] Quoted by Drummond and Wilbraham, *op. cit.*

gress, in the 1890 edition of Mrs Beeton's cookery book: 'In all tinned foods there is a danger that small lumps of solder, used in sealing the tin, may fall inside and be accidentally swallowed with the meat. In turning out a tin of soup they should be looked for in the sediment at the bottom and removed'. Mrs Beeton's disapproval did not hold back the canning industry unduly. By 1900, automatic machinery could make cans from sheet tinplate at the rate of 2,500 an hour, as against sixty cans an hour hand-made in the late 1870s. The production of cans moved out of the canning plant and into the factories of a specialized can-manufacturing industry. This was the setting in which the American Can Co was formed in 1901, and the rival Continental Can Co in 1905. After that, there was no holding back the advance of the food can – and the can-opener.

EVEN THE NAME of the collapsible tube is against it, and few people would deny that it is the least attractive form of metal packaging, once a new tube has lost its newness. Though we think of tubes today mainly in connection with toothpaste and perhaps glue or shaving cream, they were first used for artists' colours (oil paints). John Rand, an American artist, was their inventor and patentee, in 1841, and his invention soon found its first customer in the Devoe & Raynolds Co.

After this auspicious start, for some years progress was slow in America but rapid in Europe. Most of the well-known London artists' colourmen were selling paint in metal tubes by the beginning of the 1850s; some, Rowneys among them, offered tubes or the traditional bladders as alternative packages, with the new tubes rather more expensive than the bladders.

Winsor & Newton paint tube (metal), London *c.* 1845

Tubes were first machine-made in Europe and there was some export to America – especially before 1870, when A. H. Wirz set up, in the States, a tube-making machine based on a German design.

There is no record of tubes for toothpaste until the 1890s: the pioneer of this application is said to have been Dr Washington Sheffield, a New London, Connecticut, dentist – in 1892. Colgates followed his example a few years later, and carried the public with them. A few years again, and in 1900 we find Dr Sheffield making tubes for other people's products as well as his own. (*Modern Packaging* in August 1957 was to record A. H. Wirz Inc as active in Chester, Pennsylvania, and The Sheffield Tube Corporation still active in New London.)

In England, Betts had been making collapsible tubes at Holloway since 1860, and a verbose account of this firm in *Commerce* in 1900 listed the applications of Betts' tubes at that time as artists' colours, soap and shaving cream, ink, toothpaste, ointments and hair dressings.

## MATERIALS

Despite this unequivocal reference to shaving cream, it is said that William Mennen, Gerhard Mennen's son and business successor, first saw this commodity in tubes when he took a cruise round the Caribbean in early 1912; and that at that time nobody in the United States was yet marketing shaving cream in tubes. By the end of the year, Mennen was (plate 165). Thanks to metal packaging, Uncle Sam's chin would never be the same again.

# Package Design

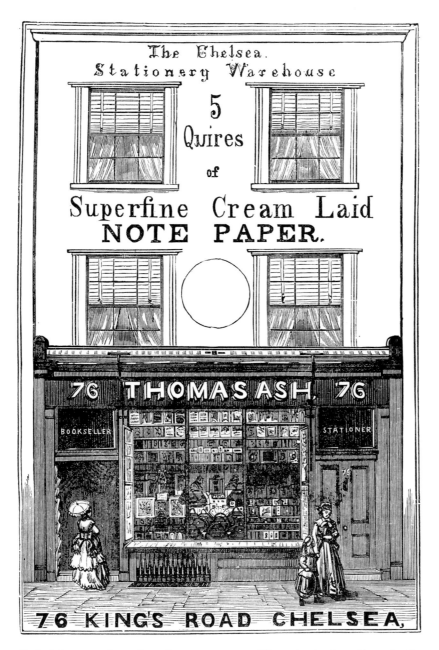

The Chelsea.
Stationery Warehouse

5

Quires

of

Superfine Cream Laid
NOTE PAPER.

76 THOMAS ASH. 76

BOOKSELLER          STATIONER

76 KING'S ROAD CHELSEA,

Label for a packet of stationery, *c.* 1870. Note the back-to-front 'u' in
'Quires' – also the circle between the first-floor windows; the wood engraving was pierced here so that prices could be inserted in type

One of several paper-mill labels designed by Dr Alexander Anderson of New York (page 95), a disciple of Thomas Bewick

# DESIGN

THE HISTORY of package design is a record of changing popular taste over the centuries. The pictures on packages, and their typography and general style, show clearly and convincingly what the public wanted at different times – or what the manufacturers of those times thought they wanted.

At no time in the period with which we are concerned was there anything *avant-garde* about package design. Competence rather than brilliance was characteristic of it; and sometimes, in illustrations especially, it was not even technically competent but engagingly amateurish. Early package designs were, to a large extent, the art of the artless – as close to folk art as designs reproduced mechanically in an industrial society could ever be (plates 63–65, 166–168).

Until the end of the eighteenth century, and indeed for thirty years after that, commerce had not acquired a 'face' of its own. The successful trader did not flaunt his success but hastened to conform to the pattern of the gentry; his shop windows were of small panes of glass like those of a gentleman's town house; his trade card was lettered in the same elegant scripts as a gentleman's visiting card; and as for packaging there was not enough of it to enable package design to acquire a style of its own: the printed paper wrapper (plate 53) looked like the trade card – as we have seen, in some instances it *was* the trade card; and the seal on an innkeeper's wine bottle was the same in character as the seal on a wine bottle made for the ducal cellars at Woburn Abbey.

The most obvious change of style in packaging at any time was the coming of colour. A few eighteenth-century wrappers were printed in red ('sanguine' *e.g.* John Jones's in plate A) where one might have expected black, but this was still monochrome, not colour in the sense of several colours used together, which was a nineteenth-century packaging innovation.

Before colour printing could be done well, at a price which commerce would pay, it was common to introduce colour into pictures by printing the outlines in black and adding each colour by hand, perhaps with stencils to speed the task; this method was used for pictures on boxtops (plate 86) as well as fashion plates, book illustrations, and pictures for framing. (Currier and Ives, whose lithographs recorded the American scene in the mid-century, at one time employed about twelve young women on hand-colouring alone.) 'Rich, lustrous colour seems to have been a passion with the Victorians, and experimenters in all mediums strove towards it.'[1] In packaging it came in an ever-widening stream from the 1830s onwards.

*Printed* colour probably made its first appearance in packaging on matchbox labels (plate 175) of the 1830s, when several London manufacturers were using designs in which the name appeared in white against a panel of solid colour. Rival firms' labels were so similar that it has been suggested by Miller Christy that they may all have been the work of one printer.

The printing of coloured pictures presented many problems, not least the maintenance of accurate 'register' between the colours as they were successively printed. There were many experiments in the eighteenth and early nineteenth centuries, and George Baxter's is generally

---

[1] Nicolette Gray: see bibliography.

(though not universally) considered to have been the first successsful solution. In 1835, when he was 31, Baxter succeeded in obtaining patent protection for his methods, including the use of oil-based inks which he mixed himself, and of an engraved steel or copper plate for the key colour; this, in effect, provided a template for the wood blocks for the other colours.

Baxter was a sensitive craftsman with a highly developed colour sense and the ambition to print large reproductions of works of art. But – despite royal approval – this did not bring him great prosperity. By the late 1830s the hot breath of his creditors had blown him into more commercial work, and later he was to produce a considerable number of box-top pictures. Orders from Thomas De La Rue for pictures to adorn the packaging of his playing cards and his 'Queen's Papeterie' stationery were a notable tribute to George Baxter's ability, for De La Rue himself had been one of the pioneers of colour printing – mainly for playing cards – about the time of Baxter's own patent.

But the best-known picture prints of the mid-century were for needle boxes – prints not very much larger than a pair of postage stamps, yet exquisite in their detail and their colouring. According to Baxter's biographer, Courtney Lewis, needle manufacturers in Birmingham, Redditch and elsewhere entered into large contracts for the supply of these prints. Unfortunately, Courtney Lewis did not record the names of the needle manufacturers concerned, so we cannot give them the credit which is due for their enlightened patronage of, literally, applied art. Some firms in the same industry bought their boxtop pictures from another London printer, Le Blond & Co (plate 87).

Needles were a notable export from Britain at this time: in *Madame Bovary* (1857) Flaubert writes of Monsieur Lheureux – the travelling draper who tempted Emma Bovary into extravagance and debt – that he 'exhiba délicatement. . . . plusieurs paquets d'aiguilles anglaises. . . .'

While Baxter was still in business in London, he had licensed a number of other printers to use his process. Le Blond was one of these, and another was J. M. Kronheim & Co – also a London firm, though founded by a German. Kronheims are said to have printed over 4,000 items between 1846 and 1878, and in this period there was hardly any type of pictorial colour work which they did not 'produce by Baxter printing.'[1] They make an appearance in the annals of packaging as early printers of chocolate-box tops for Cadburys (1870).

The change from one to two colours, and from two to many, in transfer-printing on pottery has already been noted. The fact that in 1859 wrapping papers were advertised in white, blue, lavender, pink, and other colours suggests that papermakers shared the prevailing passion; perhaps they were forced into offering such a breadth of choice by the competitive enterprise of the tinfoil manufacturers, who were not long content to produce all their foil in its natural colour but offered 'gold, silver or other metallic foil'd papers'.

THE WIDER use of colour was, however, only one of several ways in which Victorian packaging and Victorian trade generally broke away from the black-and-white gentility of the centuries before. The manufacturer was no longer content to ape the style of the upper classes – and the

---

[1] According to Fred. W. Seeley, a later manager of the firm. Unlike Baxter himself, Kronheims used metal blocks for all their colours.

vast market of unsophisticated customers toiling in the industrial towns of Britain or trailing westward across America was more likely to be tempted by the showy than by the stylish. The new plate glass in cast iron frames replaced small panes and gave a new appearance to shop windows (plates 170 to 172). And above the windows the shopkeepers' names were painted or incised or attached in the form of cut-out letters, in styles that broke away from the formal scripts and from the classic roman capitals of tradition. The new and more varied letter-forms found their way also onto the packages sold in the shops. The sign-makers and the type-designers influenced each other from quite early in the nineteenth century; the wood-block engravers and later the artists who drew designs for lithography also joined in. The introduction of display type-faces in increasing numbers made the more forceful presentation of wording on packages practicable at a time when changing taste made it desirable. For the first time since the invention of printing from movable type, the printer could buy type-faces which were not book types 'writ large' but deliberately departed from the bookish styles which had until then been regarded as the only styles for printed letter-forms.

Now there were 'Modern' faces in which the difference between thick and thin strokes was emphasized, and Fat Faces (1810) in which it was not just emphasized but exaggerated. There were Egyptian faces with broad slab serifs (1815); there were faces with no serifs at all (1816), at one time confusingly known as Antique – now Sanserif or Grotesque; and there were Tuscan faces, in which the ends of the main strokes split and spread outwards to form their own serifs (plates 174a–d).

There were also styles in which the letters were ornamented, sometimes with lining or shadow effects to give the appearance of three dimensions – the signwriters' influence? – sometimes with more elaborate ornamentation that took the letters out of the range of readability, or nearly so. There were letters that looked like tendrils, like leaves and thorns (plate 176), like twigs (plate 177). The twigs were a firm mid-nineteenth-century favourite, a style in which the type-founders (*e.g.* Figgins, *c.* 1846) lagged behind the artists. Nicolette Gray mentions rustic letters hanging like curtain-rings on the boughs of a tree; the designer of an American collar box (plate D), late in the century, went one better by hanging some letters in the trees of a parkland scene and laying others down on the surface of a stream – which of course is logical in a crazy way; if letters were twigs, they would float.

The influence of developments in printing and typography on nineteenth-century package design can hardly be overestimated. Besides all the packs which were wholly printed – wrappers, bags and fancy tins – the surface design of most others was *printed* design applied to packaging with the paste-brush: most wooden boxes, cardboard boxes, bottles and pots, and the cheaper tins, relied largely for character on printed paper labels.

And the manufacturers of packages relied equally on outside firms to print their labels or wrappers for them. Even cardboard boxmakers managed quite nicely without printing presses; Robinsons of Chesterfield were in business – in a growing and successful business – for half-a-century before they felt the need for a printing department (in the 1890s); and the Premier Box Company of Hulme, Manchester, actually sublet part of their floor-space to an independent printer who set the type for their millinery boxes (1897–1910).

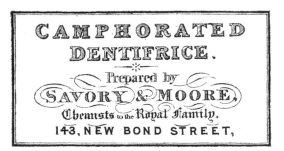

Labels dating from the 1860s or later

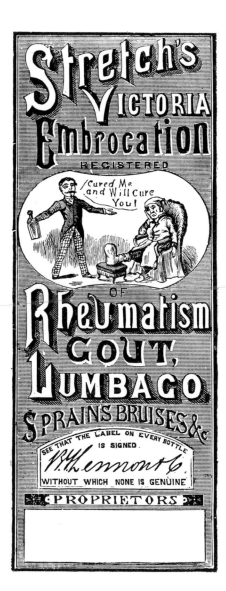

WELLCOME'S MAGIC INK.
The Greatest Wonder of the Age!
This is something entirely New and Novel!
**Directions.**
Write with quill or golden pen, on white paper. No trace is visible until held to the fire, when it becomes very black.

PREPARED ONLY BY
**H. S. WELLCOME,**
GARDEN CITY. MINN.

Crude typography in a label for H. S. Wellcome (who later emigrated from the USA to England). Before 1880

From a late nineteenth-century carton by the Britannia Folding Box Co. The printed signature 'without which none is genuine' was a characteristic of package design for many years

The exceptional firms – those which combined package-making and general printing – tended to be extraordinarily coy about the former and proud of the latter. 'Plain and ornamental job printer . . . embracing the choicest gems from the principal Type Founders of the United States' is not, perhaps, the most obvious description of Robert Gair, paper merchant and manufacturer of paper bags and hand-made cartons, but this is how Gair described himself in an advertising leaflet of 1871. Similarly in England, at a time when Mardon Son & Hall were among the country's leading bagmakers, their letterheads scarcely found space to mention a bagmaking department, and the inscription on the front of their premises ignored it completely.

'Paper bag warehouse' was not, apparently, Mardon Son & Hall's proudest claim

It is almost incredible, but true, that Burch's *Colour Printing and Colour Printers*, published in 1910 and still an accepted authority on historical aspects of its subject, makes no reference at all to tin-printing, and devotes several pages to George Baxter without even mentioning his needle-box prints. Packaged goods existed to supply material needs, and 'Printing and the material needs of man' is clearly a less noble concept that 'Printing and the mind of man': but material needs cannot be wholly neglected – even by historians.

During the nineteenth century so many different and unrelated trades were involved in package production that it is hardly surprising that package design was a Cinderella, and that when style emerged in packaging, it was usually a style which fashion had already passed by. One of the most powerful designs illustrated in these pages (plate 65) gains much of its power from the use of a display type-face which was forty or fifty years old at the time the design was printed: the frequent pictures of gold medals (plates 178–180) and wording placed on straps and scrolls bring packaging closer to the paintwork traditions of farm implements than to art in the fine or academic sense. Instances of package design as a backward art are easy to find. A biscuit tin in the shape of a vase (plate 189), dated about 1900, is decorated with Pre-Raphaelite damsels, though serious creative artists had abandoned Pre-Raphaelitism some ten years earlier. Not only fine art but the other commmercial arts of the nineteenth century generally kept one step ahead of package design: an American trade press advertisement of 1887 (plate 202) is an interesting forerunner of *art nouveau* in the tendril-like curves of its lettering and decoration, but the design of the package which it illustrates could hardly be duller. The hint of *art nouveau* in the design of the advertisement itself is advanced for its day, for the style did not reach its peak until 1895–1900.

# H. HICKSON
## Outside the "Cambridge,"

Detail from plate 65

Two interesting package designs from this period – a powder box for Yardley and a whole range of packs for Atkinson (plates 182, 185–6) – are so similar in style that one begins to wonder whether both of these English manufacturers bought their designs from the same studio – and that in Paris, perhaps, rather than London: the French were long acknowledged as the world leaders in perfumery and cosmetics, and one has only to recall the name-signs and ironwork of Paris Métro stations to be reminded that *art nouveau* enjoyed a great vogue in France between 1895 and 1900.

This style, like others before, lingered on in packaging after it was considered old-fashioned in some other fields of design: those long flower-like curves are seen in a number of packages designed around 1907–1914 – if not in their main design, at least in decorative borders (plates 103, 183 and 184).

Today *art nouveau* is still a subject for strong liking or strong disliking; whether one likes it or not, one must welcome the new life which it gave to package design, for where there was no *art nouveau*, between say 1910 and 1914, there was usually no style at all. Georgian austerity had long gone out of fashion; now Victorian richness had followed it – except perhaps from the field of metal box design, where the shapes which were technically possible were elaborate enough for anyone, and often more interesting than the surface designs printed on them (plates 141 and 144–5).

## Pictures on packages

In twentieth-century eyes it must seem that a great advantage of a pictorial package design is its ability to give a picture of the contents, and so help to sell them: but this was one of the last kinds of illustration to make its appearance in packaging.

The first pictures were usually symbols of a shopkeeper's trade or his shop-sign, or the arms of a trade guild: in the early 18th century, for example, London craftsmen who made pins were members of the Company of Pinmakers, and the badge of the Company, a portrait of Queen Elizabeth, made a handsome centrepiece for many pin papers (plate A and page 22).

People treated more naturalistically were also among the first subjects of pictures on packages. On early tobacco-wrappers there were portraits of men traditionally associated with the introduction of tobacco into England from Virginia – Captain John Smith on the wrapper of a tobacconist named Gaitskell, and the distinguished features of Sir Walter Raleigh on a paper for 'Read's *best* Virginia *Chancery Lane*' (plate 187).

Nineteenth-century British manufacturers gave the Queen's portrait and the royal arms a prominence in package designs which has not been equalled before or since

Satisfied customers, smokers with trails of wording in the manner of comic-strip balloons (plate 166), also appeared before the end of the eighteenth century.

Manufacturers did not begin to make personal appearances on their packages until the second half of the nineteenth century, the heyday of the drooping moustache (plate 148); quack medicines in particular were then considered more saleable if the quack doctor dared to show his face on the packet or label (plate 58). A less hackneyed approach was that of a Lincoln manufacturing chemist in illustrating the interior of a chemist's shop of the period – soon after his business was established in 1859. That his successors were using the design almost unchanged a hundred years later suggests that his idea cannot have been wholly wrong (plate 191).

The picture of the packer's premises had made its first appearance before the end of the eighteenth century; in the 1780s B. W. Anstie printed on his snuff-wrappers an illustration of Whistley Mill near Devizes – the water-mill in which the firm had ground snuff from 1740 onwards (plate 190). In America, several paper mills in the early nineteenth century printed detailed pictures of their premises on their wrappers (plate 57 and page 86). Factory views appeared also on many of Huntley & Palmers' biscuit tins: their early labels are relevant to industrial archaeology as well as package design, because they illustrate the rebuildings and extensions of premises which marked the firm's progress through its first century (plates 193 to 196).

But the most numerous, and possibly the most interesting, of all pictures on packages are those which have no obvious connection with the products inside the packages. The Glamour Girl must be considered the first subject in importance, though not in date, under this heading. Perhaps her first incarnation is as Dixie Queen illustrating the brand-name of an American plug cut tobacco of the Civil War period on a pack now in the Museum of Packaging Antiquities formed by Walter Landor & Associates in San Francisco. It is a notable piece of packaging in other respects also: a miniature sack of cotton printed with Dixie Queen's portrait and a lot of wording. It is said that these sacks were used for sending small amounts of tobacco to soldiers in the field (plate 188).

In English package design, the introduction of glamour is usually attributed, for praise or blame, to Richard Cadbury. His box-top pictures have already been referred to; one of his subjects was a young lady wearing a hat described as 'a partridge sitting on a nest of ermine'. This young lady and her successors no doubt explain the origin of the phrase *chocolate-box art* – a phrase which seems to have been coined even earlier than one might expect. 'If the ladies on the chocolate boxes were exactly incarnate', Max Beerbohm wrote in 1901, 'their beauty would conquer the world: yet no discreet patron of art collects chocolate-boxes.'

The chocolate-box girl was not the first subject of illustration strictly irrelevant to the package's contents. Before she was born, manufacturers had shown a news-sense worthy of Fleet Street in their choice of topical subjects. Portraits of Victoria and Albert adorned the box of Victoria congreve matches at the time of the royal wedding (1840). *A Letter from the Diggings* – the Australian goldfields, discovered in 1851 – was the subject of a Jesse Austin pot lid. The Crimean war (1854–6) provided grim inspiration for a matchbox with *The Attack on the Redan* on one side and *The Defence of the Gorge of the Malakhoff* on the other. The practice continued . . . royal anniversaries and coronations were commemorated (with tin boxes especially) (plate C) and in 1908, when the *Mauretania* was launched, this stately ship also appeared in a biscuit tin design (plate 143).

Among less topical but equally irrelevant subjects, the log cabin was a recurring theme for American package designers – nearly half a century separates the two illustrated (plates 197 and 198). An English weakness was for little girls, nursery rhyme and children's book characters (plates 82, 94 and 110). A rather sad story – sad because everyone in it acted with good intentions, and upset everyone else – concerns the reproduction of some pictures from *Through the Looking Glass* on a biscuit tin (plate 140). The story begins in 1885, when Lewis Carroll (C. L. Dodgson) wrote a letter of appreciation of some verses contributed to a woman's magazine by Mary, sister of Charles Manners, of the metal boxmaking firm of Barringer, Wallis & Manners. When, in 1891, Manners had the idea of reproducing Sir John Tenniel's *Looking Glass* illustrations on a biscuit tin, it was through Mary Manners that the approach was made – by letter to Lewis Carroll. He expressed the opinion that specimen boxes made by the firm, which she sent him, were 'of considerable artistic merit', and gave his approval. In March 1892 he was shown a proof tin, and in September of the same year he accepted Charles Manners' offer of free sample tins for 120 little friends. His own sample arrived just after he had written the letter of acceptance – and provoked a telegram cancelling it forthwith because the boxes were being despatched with Jacobs' biscuits in them and, worse, a 'vulgar advertisement' pasted inside the lid. First Manners apologized for the advertisement; next Carroll apologized for his hastiness. In the following year Manners suggested that an *Alice in Wonderland* tin might come next, but no more was heard of this project.

Sometimes the manufacturer's judgment of what pictures would appeal to his public was sound; sometimes it was not. In the 1890s an American can label upset an influential minority because it carried a picture of cherubs dancing in a ring, and it was evident that the cherubs were male. Some league of busybodies took offence at this, and the canners, Burnham & Morrill, decided to modify the design by overprinting a bright red band in lieu of fig-leaves. But the red ink was transparent, and not only revealed what it should have concealed but drew attention to it.

PICTURES on packages were seldom of great artistic merit, and their artists' names have mostly gone unrecorded. An exception is that of Dr Alexander Anderson (1775–1870) in America. As a young man, Anderson saw some engravings by Thomas Bewick, and he decided to follow Bewick's style. He graduated as a Doctor of Medicine but gave up medical practice after his whole family had died in an epidemic: and perhaps this explains why Anderson, remembered as the first wood engraver in the United States, found time to design *inter alia* a considerable number of paper-mill labels: for D. Hoogland, Long Island (*c.* 1805–10); the Bronx Mill, New York (*c.* 1812); S. & W. Meeteers', Maryland, and the Orange County Paper Mill, New York, as well as the Third River label (page 86). Most of his designs included the American eagle; on the label for Meeteers, according to Dard Hunter, Anderson copied a picture of a vatman from an English book of trades.

It was many years later before any artists of similar calibre were involved in illustrating packages in Britain (if we except Bewick's few small label designs). About 1860, the enterprising Joseph Thorley persuaded Fred Walker, R.A., to draw a farmyard scene for the packets of Thorley's cattle food (plate 201). In 1863, the printing firm of De La Rue commissioned Owen Jones, architect, author, and designer of the 1851 Exhibition's colour-scheme, to design a label for Allsopp's ales – Allsopp had built the biggest brewery in the world at Burton-on-Trent in 1860; it is known that Owen Jones was also involved in designs for Huntley & Palmers' biscuit packaging in the same decade. Almost by accident, in 1876 George du Maurier designed an Apollinaris mineral-water label, 'drawing a fancy picture of the [Apollinaris] spring on the back of the menu' at a dinner-party at which the owner of the spring was present.[1] And in the last decade of the nineteenth century, a Norfolk lad called Alfred Munnings left school at fourteen and a half to be apprenticed to Page Bros & Co Ltd of Norwich, lithographers and boxmakers. His work there (and later as a freelance) included box-top pictures for Caley's chocolates and Caley's crackers: when freelancing he designed dozens of cracker box tops, mostly in three colours and black outline, at fifty shillings a time.

With the probable exception of Owen Jones, these men were package illustrators or artists-in-packaging rather than package designers in the sense in which this term has been current

---

[1] According to a letter in *The Times* from L. Curtis, Oxford, 23 March 1934.

since the 1930s: the idea that someone with aesthetic sense and technical knowledge should be professionally responsible for all the factors affecting the appearance of a package had not gained currency in the period with which we are concerned.

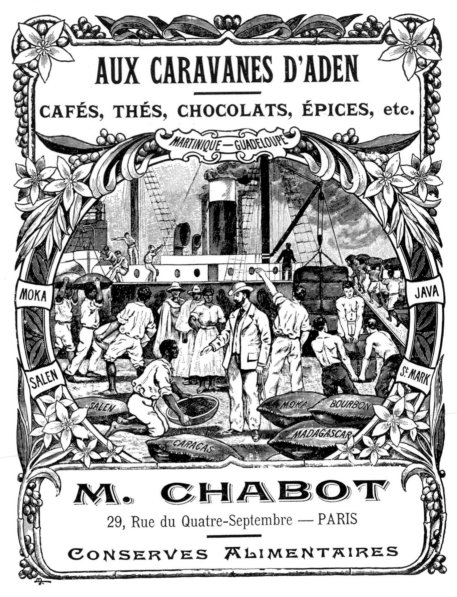

To help the smaller firms who had neither the wit to commission designs for themselves nor perhaps the money to pay for them, many nineteeenth-century package printers offered stock designs – *i.e.* designs including a space in which any manufacturer's name (or, more often, a shopkeeper's) could be inserted. French perfume labels and English tobacco labels both exist in the form in which the printer showed them to his prospective customers when canvassing for orders – with the name-space still blank. Paper bags in stock designs were also available from a relatively early date, and cartons for dried fruits from the 1900s onwards (plates 104–107). The practice was even extended to pre-printing sheets of tinplate (page 98): this material was offered in stock patterns to metal boxmakers' customers who wanted to buy tins in small quanti-

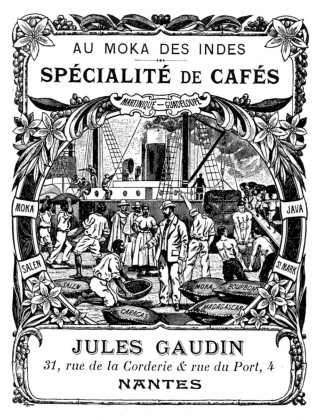

A stock design used by several grocers in different French towns on their paper bags. Probably early twentieth century

ties. The gap between the artist and his 'patron' could hardly have been wider – but the standard of design was not noticeably lower in stock packages than in packages produced to meet specific customers' requirements.

It was not very high anywhere. Said the *Box-maker's Journal* in 1899: 'There is a decided lack of style in boxmaking, [a lack of] neatness and effectiveness. . . . The rather low level is due, probably, to the box-makers' ideas being extremely subservient to those of the customers. . . . We think the experts in every trade ought to be just a little ahead of public taste, and educate the market to their ideas.' After two hundred years of inarticulateness, the note of self-criticism in one of the packaging industries is new and healthy: a good note to end on.

DESIGNS from our STOCK PATTERN CIRCULAR of Decorated Plates for making up into Tins.

Any of the Canisters specified in this Catalogue can be made from these patterns.

Special Designs, Trade Marks or Names printed if quantity is not too small.

Complete Lists forwarded on application.

Stock designs printed on tinplate by Reads of Liverpool – from their catalogue *c*. 1900–2

# BIBLIOGRAPHY

BENNING, LOTYS. *The Vegetable Canning Industry*, National Youth Administration, Indianapolis 1938

BETTENDORF, HARRY J. *Paperboard and Paperboard Containers – a History*, Chicago 1947 (first published as a series of articles in *Fibre Containers*, Chicago 1945)

CLARKE, HAROLD GEORGE. *Under-glaze Colour Picture Prints on Staffordshire Pottery (The Centenary Pot Lid Book)*, Courier Press, London 1949

CRUSE, A. J. *Match-box Labels of the World*, Robert Ross, London 1946

DRUMMOND, J. C., LEWIS, W. R., and others. *Historic Tinned Foods*, International Tin Research and Development Council, Greenford, Middlesex, second edition 1939

LONG, ROBERT P. *Package Printing*, Graphic Magazines, New York 1964

MARKS, HAYWARD. *Proofs of some early nineteenth century Woodblocks for Tea and Tobacco Papers with a note on their use*, privately printed, Kensington, London 1948

MEIGH, EDWARD. *The development of the automatic glass bottle machine*, Glass Manufacturers' Federation, London n.d. (first published in *Glass Technology*, 1 February 1960)

MOODY, B. E. *Packaging in Glass*, Hutchinson, London 1963

RENDELL, JOAN. *Collecting Matchbox Labels*, Arco Publications, London 1963

WYATT, VICTOR. *From sand-core to automation: a history of glass containers*, Glass Manufacturers' Federation, London n.d.

The following books which deal mainly with other subjects have some bearing on the history of packaging:

ADBURGHAM, ALISON. *Shops and Shopping 1800–1914*, Allen & Unwin, London 1964

BERRY, W. TURNER, and POOLE, H. EDMUND. *Annals of Printing*, Blandford Press, London 1966

BURCH, R. M. *Colour Printing and Colour Printers*, Pitman, London 1910

CAIRD, J. *English Agriculture*, quoted by M. E. SEEBOHM in *The Evolution of the English Farm*, London (second edition) 1952

CHRISTY, MILLER. *The Bryant & May Museum of Fire-making Appliances: Catalogue of the Exhibits*, Bryant & May, Bow, London 1926; and *Supplement*, 1928

CLEAVER, JAMES. *A History of Graphic Art*, Peter Owen, London 1963

COOPER, THOMAS. *The Life of Thomas Cooper written by himself*, 1873

DAVIS, DOROTHY. *A History of Shopping*, Routledge, London (and University of Toronto) 1966

DRUMMOND, J. C., and WILBRAHAM, ANNE. *The Englishman's Food*, Cape, London 1939; new edition 1957

FAIRHOLT, F. W. *History of Tobacco*, Chatto & Windus, London 1876

FLOWER, SIR NEWMAN. *Just as it Happened*, Cassell, London 1950

FLOWER, PHILIP WILLIAM. *A History of The Trade in Tin . . . a history of the origin and progress of the tin-plate trade and a description of the ancient and modern processes of manufacturing tin-plate*, George Bell & Sons, London 1880

GARNER, F. H. *English Delftware*, Faber & Faber, London 1948

GIEDION, SIEGFRIED. *Mechanization takes Command*, Oxford University Press, New York 1948

GRAY, NICOLETTE. *Nineteenth-century Ornamented Types and Title Pages*, Faber & Faber, London 1938

HANDOVER, P. M. *Printing in London*, Allen & Unwin, London 1960

HARE, W. E., and HEDGES, E. S. *Tinplate*, Arnold, London 1945

HEAL, SIR AMBROSE. *London Tradesmen's Cards of the XVIII Century*, Batsford, London 1925. *Signboards of Old London Shops*, Batsford, London 1947

HOWARD, GEOFFREY ELIOT. *Early English Drug Jars*, Medici Society, London 1931

HUGHES, G. BERNARD. *Victorian Pottery and Porcelain*, Country Life, London 1959

HUNTER, DARD. *Papermaking: The History and Techniques of an Ancient Craft*, Knopf, New York (and Pleiades Books, London) (second edition) 1947

JACOBI, CHARLES THOMAS (compiler). *The Printers Handbook of Trade Recipes, etc.* The Chiswick Press, London, 1887

LEWIS, C. T. COURTNEY. *George Baxter (Colour Printer) His Life and Work*, Sampson Low, London 1908

*George Baxter the Picture Printer*, Sampson Low, London n.d.

*The Baxter Book*, Sampson Low, London 1919

*The Le Blond Book*, Sampson Low, London 1920

LEWIS, JOHN N. C. *Printed Ephemera*, W. S. Cowell, Ipswich 1962

LUCKHURST, KENNETH WILLIAM. *The Story of Exhibitions*, Studio Publications, London & New York 1951

MAYHEW, HENRY. *London Labour and the London Poor*, London 1861

McKEARIN, GEORGE S. and HELEN. *American Glass*, Crown Publishers, New York 1941

# BIBLIOGRAPHY

MacLean, Ruari. *Victorian Book Design & Colour Printing*, Faber & Faber, London 1963

Munnings, Sir Alfred. *An Artist's Life*, Museum Press, London 1950

Penn, Margaret. *Manchester Fourteen Miles*, Cambridge University Press, London 1947

Pirtle, T. R. *History of the Dairy Industry*, Mojonnier Bros Co, Chicago 1926

Powell, Harry J. *Glass-Making in England*, Cambridge University Press 1923

Ruggles-Brise, Sheelah [Lady Ruggles-Brise]. *Sealed Bottles*, Country Life, London (and Scribner, New York) 1949

Sampson, Henry. *History of Advertising from the Earliest Times*, Chatto & Windus, London 1875

Scott, Amoret and Christopher. *Tobacco and the Collector*, Max Parrish, London 1966

Simon, André L. *The History of the Wine Trade in England*, London 1907

Thomson, Gladys Scott. *Life in a Noble Household 1641–1700*, Jonathan Cape, London, 1937

Turner, E. S. *The Shocking History of Advertising!*, Michael Joseph, London 1952

Ukers, William H. *All about Tea*, The Tea and Coffee Trade Journal Co, New York 1935

Watkins, Lura Woodside. *American Glass and Glassmaking*, Chanticleer, New York (and Max Parrish, London) 1950

Wolpe, Berthold (ed.), *Vincent Figgins Type Specimen 1801 and 1815*, Printing Historical Society, London 1967

Zucker, Irving (compiler). *A Source Book of French Advertising Art*, George Braziller, New York (and Faber & Faber, London) 1964


## COMPANY HISTORIES

Evans, Joan. *The Endless Web: John Dickinson & Co Ltd 1804–1954*, Jonathan Cape, London 1955

Darwin, Bernard. *Robinsons of Bristol 1844–1944*, E. S. & A. Robinson Ltd, Bristol 1945

Eyles, Desmond. *Royal Doulton 1815–1965*, Hutchinson, London 1965

Hayes, E. P., and Heath, Charlotte. *History of the Dennison Manufacturing Company*, Harvard University Press, Cambridge, Mass., 1929 (first published in the *Journal of Economic & Business History*, August and November 1929)

House, Jack. *A Century of Box-making: A History of Andrew Ritchie and Son Ltd from 1850 to 1950*, Maclehose, Glasgow 1950

Lief, Alfred. *The Mennen Story*, McGraw-Hill, New York 1954

Mardon, Heber. *Landmarks in the History of a Bristol Firm*, privately printed, Bristol 1918 (reprinted in *The Caxtonian*, Mardon, Son & Hall Ltd, Bristol, May 1948–June 1954)

Nowell-Smith, Simon. *The House of Cassell 1848–1958*, Cassell, London 1958

Powell, Horace B. *The Original has this Signature – W. K. Kellogg*, Prentice-Hall, Englewood Cliffs, N.J. 1956

Reckitt, Basil N. *The History of Reckitt and Sons, Limited*, A. Brown, London 1952

*Robinsons of Chesterfield Centenary*, Robinson & Sons Ltd, Chesterfield, Derbyshire 1939

Singleton, Frank. *Tillotsons 1850–1950*, Tillotson & Son Ltd, Bolton 1950

Smith, Harry Allen. *Robert Gair: a Study*, Dial Press, New York 1939

*The Delectable History of Fortnum & Mason*, London 1957

Twining, Stephen H. *The House of Twining 1706–1956*, London 1956

Williams, Iolo A. *The Firm of Cadbury 1831–1931*, Constable, London 1931


## ARTICLES AND REPORTS

Anonymous:

'An outline of packaging history' in *Shelf Appeal*, London, July and September 1938 (and correspondence November 1938)

'Betts & Co: Packaging Progress Report – 39' in *Packaging News*, London, November 1964

'Capsules and their makers' in *Commerce*, London 2 May 1900

'Dr Lyon's Tooth Powder' in *Modern Packaging*, New York, November 1951

'Evolution of the metal container' in *Chemical Products*, London, June 1959

'From Cracker Barrel to Supermarket' in *Modern Packaging Encyclopaedia*, New York 1946–7

'Packaging as it was 60 years ago' in *Packaging Review*, London, June 1957 (the sixtieth anniversary issue of the former *Box Maker's Journal*)

'The history of box making' in *The Paper Container*, London, April, May and June 1922

Carlton, William J. 'In the Blacking Warehouse' in *The Dickensian*, London, January 1964

Davis, Alec. 'In search of packaging history' in *Sales Appeal*, London, January–February 1953

'The picture on the pack' in *Penrose Annual*, London 1956

'Early days of package design' in *Graphis*, Zurich, No. 74, 1957

'History printed on tin' in *Country Life*, London 7 December 1961

'Chocolate-box beauties' in *Country Life*, London, 5 December 1963

Drew, Nicholas. 'A neglected world for black and white' in *Art and Industry*, London, June 1940

# BIBLIOGRAPHY

GRAY, MILNER. 'The History and Development of Packaging', paper to the Royal Society of Arts, reprinted in the Society's *Journal*, London 5 May 1939. A generous acknowledgment by Milner Gray to E. F. HERBERT may suggest that Herbert was the author of the *Shelf Appeal* articles noted above.

HUGHES, THERLE. 'Old English Playing Cards' in *Homes & Gardens*, London, January 1952

HUNTER, DARD. 'American Paper Labels' in *Gutenberg Jahrbuch*, Mainz 1951

LONGYEAR, WILLIAM. 'Contemporary Labels' in *Modern Packaging*, New York, December 1947

LOTHIAN, AGNES. 'Vessels for Apothecaries: English Delft Drug Jars' in *The Connoisseur Year Book*, London/New York 1953

PFISTER, ARNOLD. 'The beginnings of Printed Graphic Art' in *Graphis*, Zurich, No. 39, 1952

REINER, IMRE. 'Purposeful Packing' in *Graphis*, Zurich, No. 1/2, 1944

RUDGLEY, R. F. 'Probing the past' [of pharmaceutical packaging] in *Institute of Packaging Journal*, Wembley Park, Middlesex, September 1963

SEELEY, FRED. W. 'Baxter colour prints: How they were produced', lecture reported in the *British & Colonial Printer & Stationer*, London, 12 March 1908

WRIGHT, LEE. 'Lithographic progress: Radical changes in presses and processes in the past 40 years', lecture reported in *Printing World*, London, 12 August 1959

# General Index

*Figures in italic refer to plates; A, B, C, D, to colour plates*

# INDEX

# INDEX

# INDEX

# INDEX

# Name Index of Package Manufacturers

package printers and packaging material suppliers

# Name Index of Package-using Firms

manufacturers, shopkeepers, merchants, bottlers, brewers, etc.

# INDEX

# INDEX

1 Shallow ointment pot for 'Waller & son Guilford' – chemists in Guildford about the end of the eighteenth century – here contrasted with the plain uninscribed gallipots which were typical of earlier tin-glazed earthenware (page 37)

2 Pedestal pots for Singleton's eye ointment made at Lambeth and used by, *left to right*, the first known Singleton (Thomas, 1700–79); his son William, his great-grandson William Singleton Folgham (who flourished *c.* 1816–26); and Selina Folgham's husband, Stephen Green (fl. 1826–58). The last design shows a change from painting to transfer-printing for the wording, which was still blue on white (page 38)

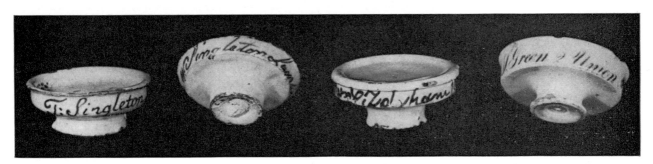

3 Blue-and-white pots for prepared mustard; *right*, used by William Wyatt at No. 11 King Street, about 1780; *left*, used by Wyatt at Soho Square, perhaps earlier. Both pots bear the cypher *GR* for George III, 1760–1820

4 Small square jars for snuff, with transfer-printed
lettering and decoration, used by Fribourg & Treyer,
1820–30

5 Chutney jar of Crosse & Blackwell, late West &
Wyatt, *c.* 1830. There are small finger-grips at the
sides of the jar at its widest point. The neck is
coloured blue; the wording is in black – with an
effective contrast between heavy Egyptian capitals
and elegant script

6 Paper-labelled blacking pot from the warehouse of G. Lamerte, who took over the business of Jonathan Warren and ran it from Mansell Street, London, between 1827 and 1832. In 1824 Charles Dickens (to whom the Lamertes were related) had had the job of covering and sealing blacking pots such as this – at the age of 11–12, for a wage of six or seven shillings weekly (page 41)

7 A less time-worn paper label (or probably a proof of one) used in 1831 for another of Lamerte's products

# Articles for the Toilet,

## SOLD BY MOST PERFUMERS AND HAIR DRESSERS

Price in Pots

2s. 6d. and 4s,

and perfumed with

OTTO of ROSE,

3s. and 5s.

Price in Bottles

3s 6d, 7s 6d, 10s 6d

and £1 1s,

and perfumed with

OTTO of ROSE,

4s 6d, 9s, 12s and 25s

## FOR THE GROWTH OF HAIR.

This article is procured from the animal in its native climate : it being known to possess more vivifying properties when so procured, than when the animal is in a domesticated state. It is of the very finest quality ; and is sent out without any admixture, except a little perfume to keep it sweet : and for the growth of hair, it is no doubt far superior to any thing hitherto known. Also for dressing the hair it is very pleasant and useful, cleaning the head from scurf, and making the hair beautifully soft and glossy.

*⁎* As many articles are sold as Bear's Grease, which are mere deceptions, being only strong rancid fats mixed with pungent essential oils, and are extremely deleterious, and some of the counterfeits so closely imitate the genuine, that it requires a near inspection to perceive the difference. Several of the counterfeits are a *fac simile* of his pot, with the word '*genuine*' instead of the name 'ATKINSON.' His is enclosed in a wrapper, with his signature and address ; and the pots have a bear on the top, surrounded with a circle, and the words '*Atkinson's Bear's Grease for the Growth of Hair,*' and underneath the price 2s. 6d. or 4s.' The above is also perfumed with Otto of Rose, at an extra price.

## Atkinson's Vegetable Dye,

For changing Grey or Red Hair to a permanent Brown or Black.

## ATKINSON'S OLD BROWN WINDSOR SOAP.

It is made of the best materials in the most approved manner, and is very highly perfumed, and being kept till very old, it not only goes twice as far as new Soaps, but is so very mild, that it more resembles a compound of almonds, than an Alkaline Soap : and to those whose skin is tender it is peculiarly adapted, and where the skin is hard, or rough from neglect, labour, the use of strong caustic soaps, &c. It soon removes such imperfections, and makes it white, soft, and even. Price, in half-pound packets, 1s. 6d. pounds 2s. 6d.

### ATKINSON'S CONCENTRATED ESSENCE OF LAVENDER,

Prepared six times the strength of best Lavender Water, free from all impyreuma of spirit and unsophisticated with the sickly admixture of musk, ambergris, &c. It being simply the finest Lavender flowers distilled to a powerful essence, it is particularly adapted for sick or crowded rooms, and the usual purposes of lavender water.

## ATKINSON'S DEPILATORY,

For removing superfluous hair from the face, neck, or arms, which it does in about five minutes, leaving the skin softer and whiter than before the application. Price 5s.

## HUDSON'S BOTANIC TOOTH POWDER AND TINCTURE.

These dentifrices are generally known for their efficacy and innocence. They eradicate the scurvy and tarter from the gums ; make the teeth, however yellow, beautifully white ; fasten such as are loose ; and if used constantly, will entirely supercede the necessity of a dentist, and preserve the teeth to the latest period of life. They possess the same properties, but the tincture acts more speedily, and is an infalliable remedy for the tooth-ache. Price 2s. 9d. each.

## ATKINSON'S CURLING FLUID,

### OR VEGETATIVE HAIR OIL.

This article has been very extensively patronised by the nobility and gentry for more than twelve years ; it is allowed to be the most elegant article ever invented for giving the hair a beautiful gloss in dressing. It nourishes and improves the growth, makes it, however harsh, soft and glossy as silk, and keeps it in curl during exercise or damp weather. Price 3s. 6d. 10s. 6d. and 1l. 1s.

## ATKINSON'S AMBROSIAL SOAP.

A very highly perfumed and mild soap, divested of all caustic properties, by a peculiar and expensive process. Price 1s. a square, or 10s. 6d. a dozen for washing, and prepared with Naples soap for shaving, in cakes at 9d. 1s. and 1s. 6d. each. The above articles have the following sigature—

*Jas. Atkinson.*

Essence of Millefleur, Bouquet, Marechalle, Resida, Violet, Tubereuse, and a variety of others. Huiles Antiques, or Oils for the Hair, in Rose, Jasmine, Orange, Cassia, &c. Powders, Pomatums, Honey Water, Almond Paste, Milk of Roses, and every other article in Perfumery. Also a great variety of Brushes and Combs of every description. Cut Glass Bottles, Shaving Boxes, Musical Boxes, Toothpicks, Double Pins, Sponge, Fans, Snuff Boxes, Razors, Bead Purses, and various fancy articles.

8

The advertising leaflet of James Atkinson, 8, with its
Bewick cut, shows the importance which Atkinson attached to his bear's-grease hair dressing. Its package, 9,
was a pot with printed design in black and a gold
border; it was supported in the shops by pottery figures
of a bear, 10, made for Atkinson by Wood and Caldwell
(fl. 1790–1818). The pot was still in use on a small
scale in 1934, at least a century after its introduction.
Atkinson was by no means the only packer of bear's
grease (pages 38–9) nor the only one to use transfer-
printed pot lids

9

10

11 Toothpaste pot of the 1860s: pink with pattern in red and lid printed in black

12 View of Trinidad on a pot for Frys. Filled with chocolate paste, it sold at *2s 8d* (1853–4)

13 Cocoa-paste pot, in monochrome, which Cadbury Bros used soon after they received the warrant of Royal appointment in 1853

Transfer-printed pot-lids from the Staffordshire Potteries for H. P. & W. C. Taylor of Philadelphia (1876?: see page 40). The buffalo-hunt scene, 14, is based on a painting by George Catlin. 'Washington crossing the Delaware', 15, was reproduced on a lid of the same size – about 5 in. diameter; and in black only on a smaller lid

16 Relish pot, probably used by Crosse & Blackwell, commemorating the Great Exhibition of 1851: see also plate 173

17 With a portrait of the young Victoria, this pot, introduced c. 1853, was produced in small quantities until 1940

18 Doulton pottery boxes for Huntley & Palmers' biscuits, with nursery-rhyme illustrations. Early twentieth century

19 Pot for Soyer's Relish, probably *c.* 1870, with portrait of Alexis Soyer. This famous chef had marketed his first sauces in 1848

20 White earthenware pot for Keiller's Dundee marmalade, with oak-leaf garland and wording in black. This design has been in use, with only minor changes, for many years – perhaps since the firm's establishment in 1797

21 Whisky jar by Govancroft Potteries, Glasgow. Pottery came before glass as a packaging material for 'Scotch'

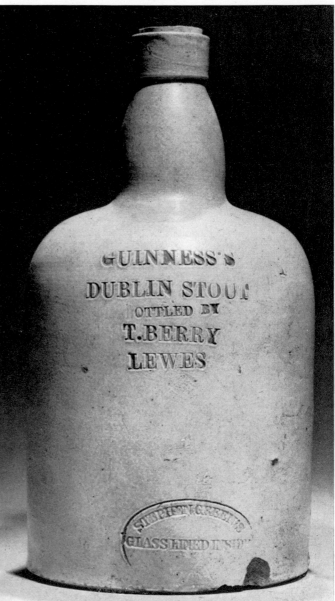

22 Guinness's Dublin Stout jar by Stephen Green of Lambeth (page 41). The wording was apparently stamped into the soft clay with printer's type: see also plates 23 and 24 overleaf. The glass lining mentioned in the oval stamp was a leadless glaze also known as Bristol glaze

23 Mid-nineteenth century brown stone-ware pot for Crosse & Blackwell

24 Early nineteenth-century varnish jars of Denton & Jutsum (established 1789), makers of the first coach varnish for railways. They used jars of various sizes from a quart to five gallons

25a

25 On the seal of this bottle (shown larger at 25a) are the date
1657, the letters 'RPM' – probably the initials of an innkeeper
and his wife – and a profile in which some observers have seen a
resemblance to King Charles I. The bottle may have been made
for a King's Head tavern. Height 9 in.; found at Wellingborough; now in the Northampton Museum

26 Wine-bottle sealed with the initials of Daniel and Anne Prince.
The Prince family owned the Mermaid Tavern, Oxford, from about
1692 to 1709. There is a mermaid at the centre of the seal, a book on
the left for the University and an ox on the right for the City of
Oxford. Found, 17 feet down, during excavations in Oxford in 1950

27 Sealed bottle in clear amber glass, 11¾ in. high, for EDW. S.
SAYRES EXTRA FINE OIL, PHILADELPHIA. Edward Sayre was in
business as a merchant at 129 South Front Street, Philadelphia in 1837

29 'Historical flasks' for whisky were made in
America from the 1820s to the 1870s. The McKearins
comment: 'The great number of designs in which
these flasks were molded would seem to indicate a
state of keen competition between glassmakers and
also between purveyors of hard liquor'. This quart-
size bottle of *c*. 1840, with George Washington's
portrait moulded in the light blue glass, was made at
the Dyottville (formerly Kensington) Glass Works
at Kensington, Philadelphia (page 45)

28 Bottle for CHESTNUT GROVE WHISKEY, C.W. [Charles
Wharton] made at the Whitney Glass Works, New Jersey
1850

30 Parchment-capped, the phial on the right has a handwritten tied-on tag but the one on the left is labelled, with a crudely printed coat of arms on the label. Drug phials such as these were the forerunners, in the seventeenth and eighteenth centuries, of later patent-medicine bottles in which the label covered most or all of the glass: see below and plate 58

31 Mrs Winslow's Syrup, distributed by the Lafayette Drug Co Inc, of Jersey City, was described on the label as 'a simple old fashioned laxative . . . useful in relief of such symptoms as wind colic and sour stomach due to constipation in infants and young children'. This shrouded bottle (probably early twentieth century) is represented in the Museum of the Container Corporation of America and in the American Museum in Britain

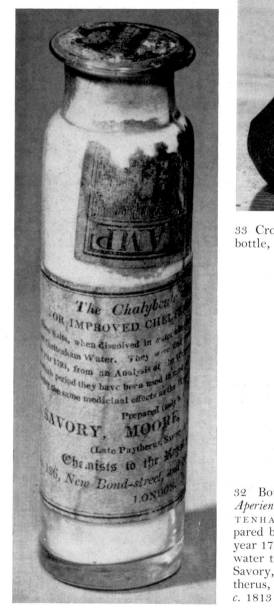

34 Bottle – of a shape most often used for snuff – for Dr Thomas Ritter's Powdered Jalap (a purgative drug made by crushing the roots of a Mexican climbing plant). $4\frac{1}{4}$ in. high. New York, mid-nineteenth century

33 Crosse & Blackwell essence bottle, in use *c*. 1855

32 Bottle for '*The Chalybeate Aperient*, OR IMPROVED CHELTENHAM SALTS . . . First prepared by Paytherus & Co in the year 1793, from an analysis of the water taken from the Old Well.' Savory, Moore & Co, late Paytherus, Savory, & Co, London *c*. 1813

35 Snob appeal in food labelling: 'The King of Oude's Favorite Sauce . . . Introduced from Oude 1825'. The name of the bottler, Hickson, is moulded in the glass

36 Bottle labels of similar date to 35. John Johnson is mentioned in Bath directories for 1833 and 1837; his label depicts York House, Bath (now the Royal York Hotel), built in 1765–9

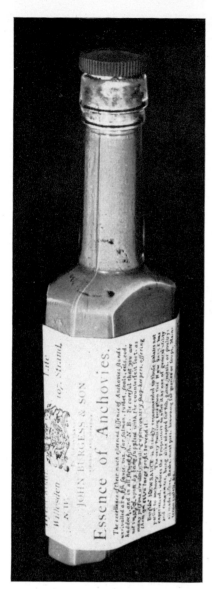

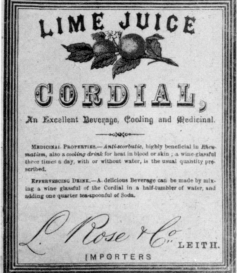

40 Early example of a shaped label:
c. 1898

38 L. Rose's label c. 1870. Later
versions are seen in plate 200 and
on page 44

37 The label on this Essence of
Anchovies bottle has been modified
in detail but is still the same in
feeling as at the time of its introduction, when long-tailed s's were
still used. The firm of Burgess,
established in 1760, advertised in
the first issue of *The Times*, 1788

39 The Bass pale ale label has at least two claims to fame: its inclusion
in Edouard Manet's *Bar at the Folies-Bergère* (1881), from which a
detail is reproduced here; and the fact that it was the first registered
trade mark in Britain (1875). It is said that a representative of Bass
spent the night on the steps of the registrar's office to be sure of getting
first place in the Trade Marks Register. The same trade mark is seen on
a poster c. 1898 in plate 207

41                42

43                44

All these bottles were blown in two-piece moulds. 41, 5⅝ in. high in clear amber glass. The name of HUTCHINS & MASON KEENE N H was apparently too much for the mould-maker: both Ss are back to front. 42–44 all approximately 4½ in. high in olive green glass. 42, for Abial A. Cooley, *c.* 1841. Besides plain glass bottles such as this he used bottles with 'A A COOLEY HARTFORD' moulded-in. 43, for Andrew Bostwick, blacking and ink manufacturer at Albany in 1833. Whatever the quality of the contents, the typographical label design undoubtedly had panache. 44, for A. Ensign, West-Hartland

# THE FIRST LABELS

More than two-thirds of all books printed in the fifteenth century were printed either in Germany or in Italy, with more than 4,000 books or editions from Venice alone, and it is hardly surprising that the two earliest known examples of printed packaging, both thought to be of the mid-sixteenth century, come from Germany and from Venice. Bernhart the paper-maker's label design, 45, was no doubt printed at the centre of a sheet of wrapping paper (like the nineteenth-century example, plate 57). The Italian label, 46, was probably pasted on the wrappers of bales of silk or other fabric, or on the material itself. The letter-forms and the decorative border on this label have something in common with Venetian book title-pages of the period (e.g. *Le Trasformationi*, 1553, reproduced as plate 91 in Stanley Morison's *Four Centuries of Fine Printing*).

These early labels are notable also as examples of early pictorial advertising; they were printed long before trade cards or illustrated newspapers became common

45

46

47 The earliest known *dated* example, 1669

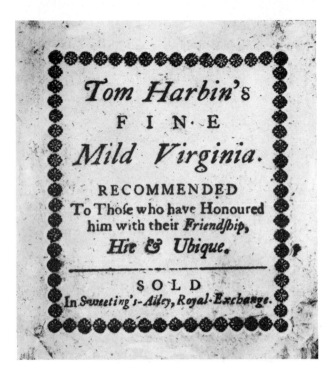

48 Eighteenth-century typography. Again the design reflects the influence of book title-pages

TOBACCO PAPERS
FROM THREE
COUNTRIES

49 Engraved: probably late eighteenth century

50 Tobacco paper from Berwick upon Tweed
  in use in 1789

51 Engraved design from Holland

52 Norwegian wrappers for 'Strong American' and other tobaccos, in use in the nineteenth century

53 Front of a paper packet for Bowen's Sago Powder, London *c.* 1780 (page 51)

54 Trade cards served many purposes. Between 1818 and 1827 Reeves used them as labels pasted inside the lids of wooden boxes of paints

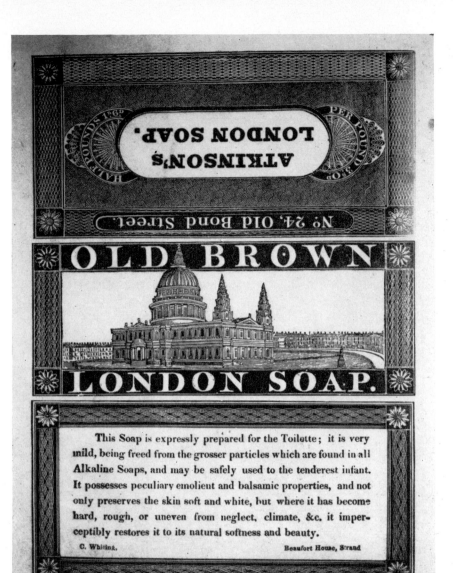

55 Soap wrapper of *c.* 1829: the words ATKINSON'S LONDON SOAP printed in black from type, the rest of the design in brown from an engraved metal plate

56 Nineteenth-century pin paper, simulating embossing, for J. Vick

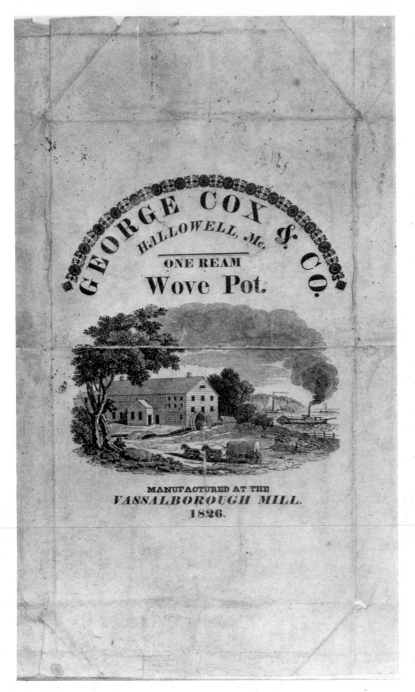

57 Early dated example of an American papermaker's wrapper.
('Pot' was a paper size)

58 This paper wrapper from Connecticut completely conceals the glass
bottle which it protects

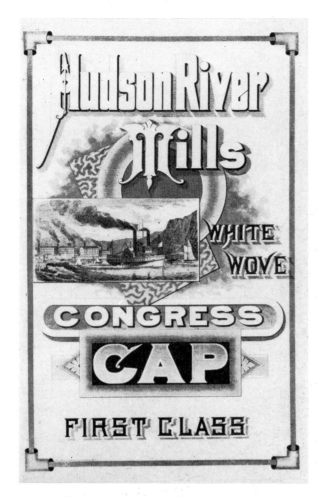

59 Papermaker's label of 1886, lithographed by Deutz Bros, New York. Comparison with plate 57 makes painfully obvious the decline in design standards which went with sixty years of technical progress

60 Wrapper designed shortly after royal visits to Doncaster in 1851–2 – still in use a century later. (The background is a leaflet in similar style, especially in its headline typography, from the King's Lynn Museum collection – dated August 1854)

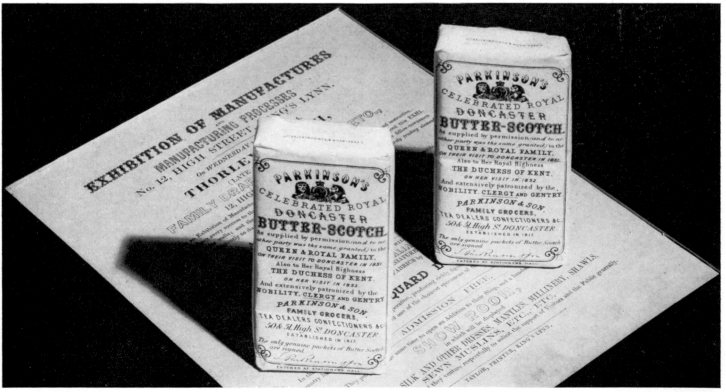

61 Wrapping paper (or perhaps the front of a large paper bag) from a shop at Ely, Cambridgeshire. The depth of the printed design is 11½ in.; immediately below the illustration, apparently engraved with it as part of the block, is the imprint of C. Robinson & Co London – presumably Crescens Robinson & Co, who described themselves as 'wholesale stationers, paper bag & account book makers, lithographers & printers', of 80 Borough Road, London S.E., in 1877

62 The imprint on this wrapping paper shows that it was printed at one of the first lithographic printing works in America, established at Washington Street, Boston, by John Pendleton – who had brought lithographic stones and other necessities of his trade from Paris
Nathaniel Currier (1813–88: see page 87) started his apprenticeship here in 1828
Pendleton's successors claimed that he had been the first litho. printer in the United States, in 1823; others – notably Barnett & Doolittle of New York – have disputed this claim

63

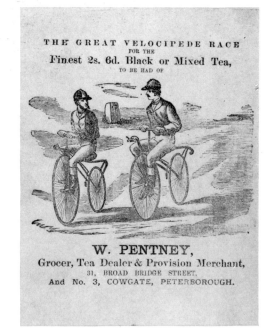

64

The 1860s were the heyday of the velocipede. In package design, the craze was reflected in a matchbox label (for Palmer's Velocipede Vesuvians) which showed Mr Punch and Dog Toby riding 'boneshakers', and in these grocers' bags, 63, 64, which were probably illustrated from printers' stock blocks. W. Pentney was in business in Broad Bridge Street, Peterborough, 1869–76

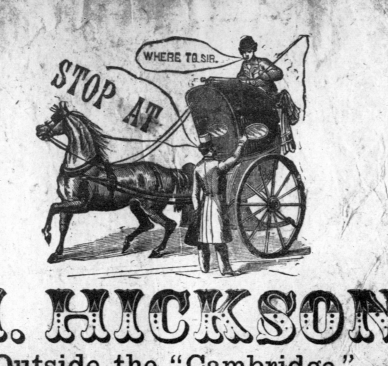

65 Paper bag used apparently by a street trader with a regular pitch 'Outside the "Cambridge"', a London pub (now Watneys'). His name is in a Stephenson Blake type-face of about 1849 – see also page 92 – but the costume and the Sherlock Holmes atmosphere of the stock-block illustration suggest that the bag cannot have been printed before the 'nineties. Leonard Fisher, Senior, was in a business as a paper-bag maker and printer at 26 Chalton Street in 1893 (with another Leonard Fisher, presumably Junior, at 103 Chalton Street). The wording gives no indication of the bag's contents: was L. Fisher the original winkle-bag printer?

66 Shopping scene of the period on a bag for E. E. Oldham
(now Oldhams Caterers Ltd) of Newark, Nottinghamshire, *c.* 1880

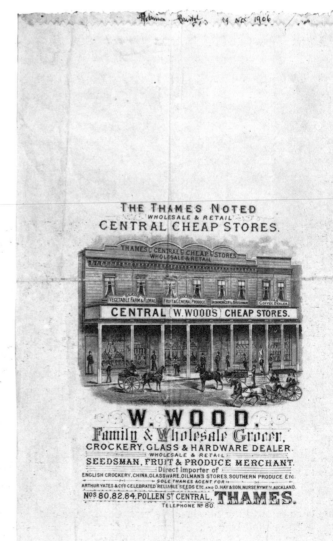

67 Bag for a general store at Thames, New Zealand, 1906.
Both by E. S. & A. Robinson, Bristol

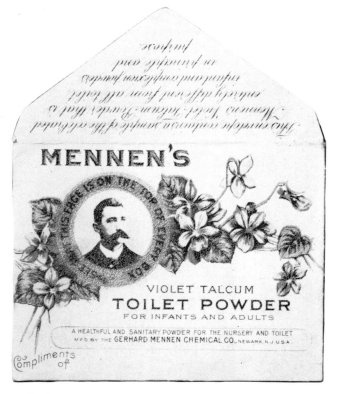

68 Packet for free samples of Mennen's toilet powder. Newark, New Jersey, early twentieth century

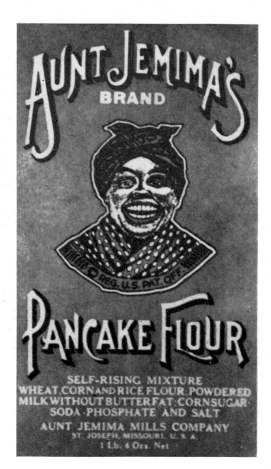

69 The original package for Aunt Jemima's Pancake Flour – a paper bag printed in black and dark red. St Joseph, Missouri, 1889

70 Tea packets by E. S. & A. Robinson for Joseph F. Mart & Co, of Chapel Street 'Opposite the Town Hall', Salford, Lancashire, and for D. E. Evans of Gwernogle, Wales, c. 1900

71 French reward for British inventiveness: at the Paris Universal Exhibition of 1889 a silver medal was awarded to Bibby & Baron for one of their early bag-making machines (page 59)

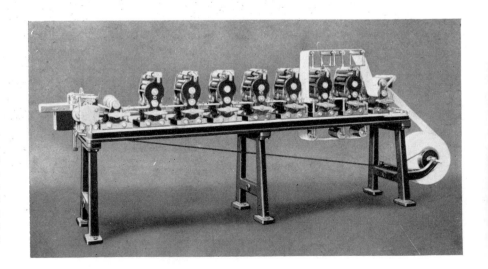

72 The carton printing machine developed over a decade by Louis Chambon (1861–1932) was first seen at the 1900 Paris Exhibition, where it won a *grand prix*. Chambon's basic idea was to mount several units on one base and drive them rigidly to produce printed cartons straight from the reel of raw material (page 33)

73 A Crier of Band Boxes – one of the 'numerous copper plates' in *Modern London; being the history and present state of the British metropolis*, printed for Richard Phillips, 1805

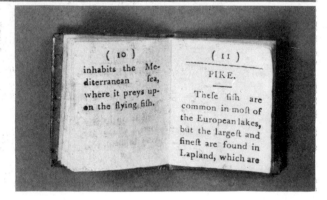

74 Wooden box with paper-labelled sliding
lid for The Infant's Cabinet of Fishes (page
62), seen here with some of its contents.
London, 1801

75 The label design is a good deal more sophisticated than the wire-hinged wooden box which it decorates. American, probably first half of nineteenth century

76 Chip box with paper label for *Mr* H. Green of Vine Valley, by 'North and company grape box manufacturers'. The absence of capital letters after the N was probably due to a shortage of capitals in the printer's stock of type rather than a liking for *avant garde* typography

77 Chase, Isherwood & Co were the proprietors of the Buckeye Tobacco Works, Toledo, Ohio (Ohio being the Buckeye State); they made both smoking and chewing tobaccos. Established in 1862, they were considered 'worthy of commendation; reliable in all transactions' (*Resources & Industries of Ohio*, 1882)

78 Another early American wooden box, from Jamestown, N.Y.

79 Label for a wooden cigar-box, chromo-lithographed by Geo. S. Harris & Sons of New York, Philadelphia and Chicago; copyright New York 1893. Brand-name and portrait make an odd combination

80 Miniature crate for chocolate drops (approximately 6 in. long). Paris, early twentieth century

81 Paper-covered wooden box for flower seeds from Mandeville & King, Rochester. Printed by Brett Litho Co, New York

82 Paper-labelled lid of a wooden 'sell-out' box for Cadbury's *c.* 1913. The same picture was also printed on small cartons

83 Paper-lined and paper-covered box, in black, red and white, for licorice. Similar to many nineteenth-century pill boxes: in use in France in 1966

84 Fancy round box for D. F. Tayler & Co's hairpins, 1893

85 Box for Letchford's tapers; cardboard, covered in patterned paper. London, mid-nineteenth century

86 Rigid cardboard box for T. & J. Smith's quill pens, with narrow gold border round the lid. The floral design was printed in black outline, the colour added by hand. London, probably *c.* 1840

87 Needle boxes were decorated with finely detailed colour prints (page 88). *Top left*, base of an outer box by Baxter: *right*, lid of an outer box by Le Blond. The ten small boxes which fitted into this outer – Le Blond's 'Regal' set of 1852–3 – are also shown.

88 Cardboard collars in cardboard boxes: a late nineteenth-century fashion note

89 Cardboard hatbox used by Henry Heath, at the 'City End' of Oxford Street, London, 1884. Besides illustrating two fashionable hats of the season, the label included quotations from *The Queen* in praise of Heath's products

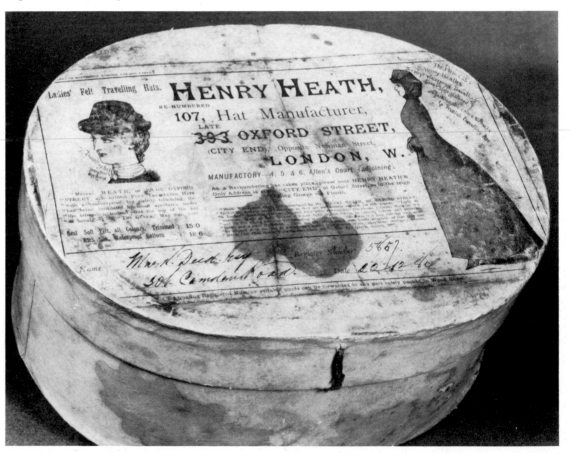

90 The phonograph record boxes in this group are (left to right) Edison 1900 – made by Seeley Tube & Box Co, Newark, New Jersey, with letter-press-printed label in green and gold-bronze by Nevins-Church Press, New York; Lakeside *c.* 1910 for Montgomery Ward – also with two-colour paper label; Edison Blue Amberol 1912 – by Seeley, with letterpress-printed label in blue, gold-bronze and sepia. [Foreground: sweet tin from France, early twentieth century]

91 Shell-and-slide box for butterscotch. An early twentieth-century package whose exotic lettering perhaps reflects the interest in Japan which was widespread at the time – *The Mikado* had first been seen in 1885

92 The earliest known Fry's chocolate box, 1868

93 Typical Fry's boxes of the 1870s

94 Painted in the autumn of 1868 and used on chocolate cream boxes about New Year 1869, Richard Cadbury's first box-top design depicted 'a blue-eyed maiden, some six summers old . . . The picture [was] got up in colours by Messrs Goodall and Co, of London' (page 65)

95 A later chocolate-box girl – on a Cadbury box-top of 1913–14

Cadbury's
FRUIT FLAVOURED
CHOCOLATE
Cremes
426                    ½ ℔ Box, about 10 to Oz

96 Meanwhile chocolates had become rather less of a luxury: Cadburys were packaging their small chocolate creams in this carton by Tillotsons c. 1910

97 Flat packet for Sahara cigarettes, *c.* 1894, made for Wills of Bristol by Mardon Son and Hall, also of Bristol

98 and 99  Cartons for Ogden's cigarettes by Tillotsons of Bolton, *c.* 1910

100 Trade mark registered in 1891;
the centrepiece of Navy Cut package
designs for many years

102 The technical competence of this carton,
c. 1909, cannot hide the low standard of
lettering and illustration which was common
in the first quarter of the present century –
evident in plates 153, 163, 167 also

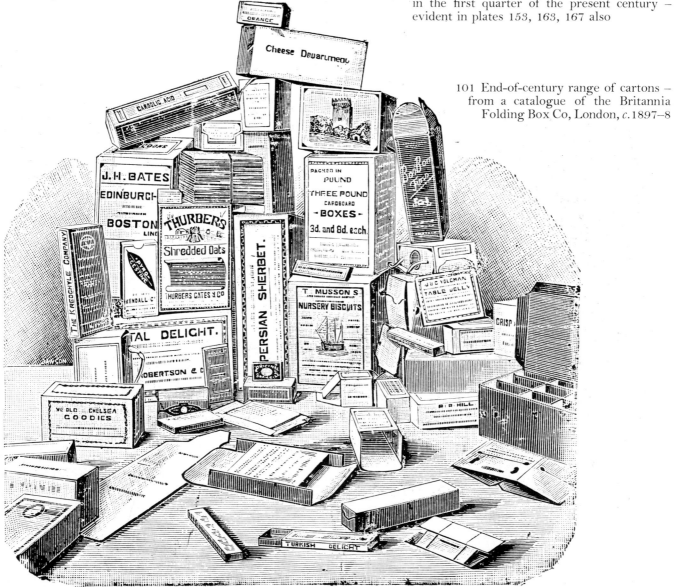

101 End-of-century range of cartons –
from a catalogue of the Britannia
Folding Box Co, London, c. 1897–8

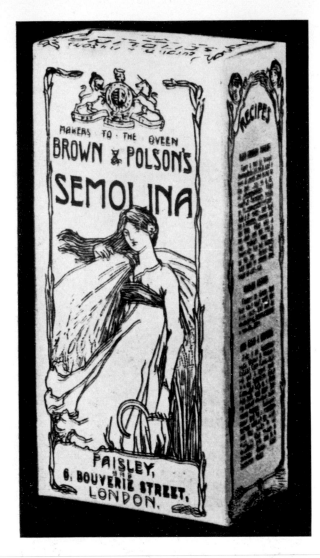

In 1879 Samuel Cropper (page 67) started in business in London as a merchant and manufacturer of bags and cartons. In 1893 his firm became Cropper & Co Ltd. 103, 108, 109 are some of its products, *c.* 1907

103                    104

104–107 Dried fruit cartons by E. S. & A. Robinson of Bristol, in stock designs used by various retailers. 104 is an early example of a Christmas pack (compare plates 118, 145, 167, 176)

105                    106                    107

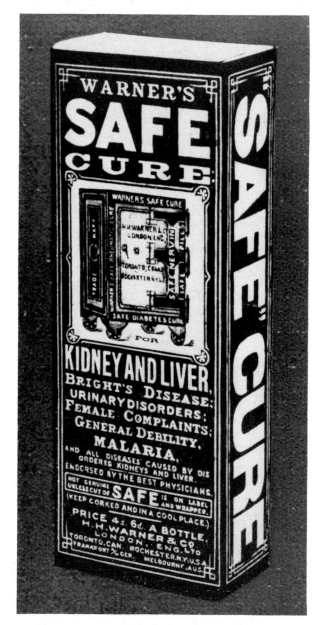

108 Cropper's registered design for egg boxes. It was also developed into an electric lamp carton for Ediswan

109 Pictorial punning on a Safe Cure carton for H. H. Warner & Co, London, Eng, Ltd. A paper-labelled bottle for Warner's Safe Remedy, with a New York address, is in the Container Corporation of America Museum

110 Early example of a photograph reproduced on a package – by Tillotsons, who made 175-screen half-tone blocks as early as 1897. The illustration was probably printed letterpress, the rest of the design by direct lithography. c. 1910

111 Presentation needle case holding four small packets of needles – a fantasy of paper work

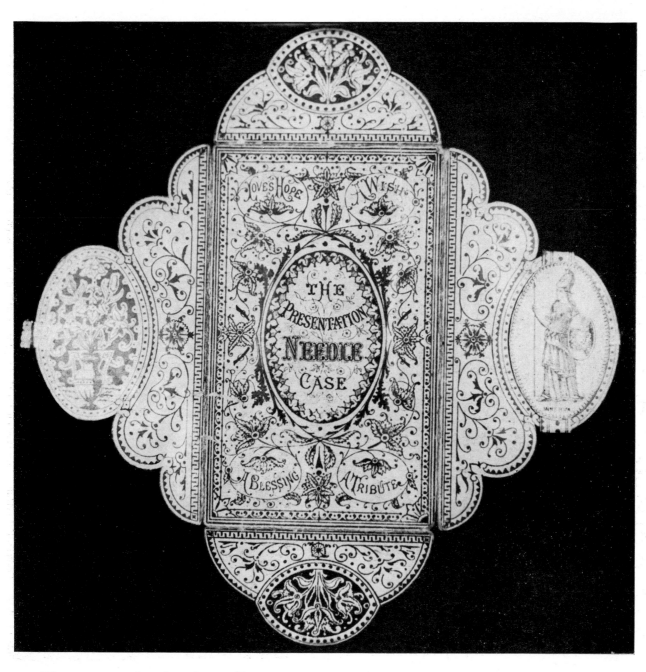

111a The same, turned to show the outside

112 The first boxmaking factory in Ireland –
from a print of 1849. The factory had been
opened in 1840 by Austin & Co of London,
at Clonakilty, 36 miles from Cork. Its
principal products were matchboxes, taken
to Cork by horse-drawn wagons

En troisième lieu—et c'est là peut-être
le plus grand avantage—l'espace qu'elles
occupent est infinitésimal si on le compare
à celui que prennent les boîtes montées ;
en réalité, elles n'occupent qu'un peu plus
d'espace qu'une quantité semblable de

Cutting Machines.
Machines à découper,
Cortadoras mecánicas.

papier d'emballage. L'illustration page 2
montre une pile de 60 boîtes à plat
n'occupant que la même hauteur qu'une
seule boîte montée prête à être employée.

113 Belt-driven cutting machines in the
works of Cropper & Co Ltd, Southwark
Bridge Road, a few years after they moved
there from Fann Street (1898). The illustration is from their export catalogue which
included captions in three languages and
several full-colour illustrations

114 The first strawboard mill in Britain – St Louis Park Mills, Purfleet, Essex, established by Maurice Cartiaux in the 1880s (later Thames Board Mills)

115 The Actien-Gesellschaft für Cartonnagen-Industrie claimed to be the largest firm in the world manufacturing exclusively box-making machinery. Holder of 700 patents, it took legal action in 1897 to enforce several of these, including a patent for metal edges which more than twenty firms had infringed. The Cartonnagen-Industrie machine shown here was advertised in the *Box-maker's Journal*, also in 1897, by the firm's British agents, Hugh Stevenson & Sons, Manchester (page 63)

**THE ONLY MACHINE MADE** that will Cut, Crease, Punch, Shape, Print, and Emboss Folding Boxes at one operation.

The process is as simple and no more costly than printing alone.

Over **40** on Order

Capacity—**40,000** Boxes per day

Over **40** on Order

116 Elaborate rigid box for ladies' handkerchiefs, used by L. Dinkelspiel & Co, San Francisco, *c*. 1870

117 Set-up box, in black and white, for the American Pin Co, Waterbury. Late nineteenth century

118 Carton for 48 Christmas candles by the Standard Oil Co. Before 1911

119 Box for a children's game, with paper label on lid. Selchow & Righter, New York, early twentieth century

120 Perhaps the oldest *current* package design, the label for Ship Brand sailmakers' needles, top left, had been 'in use for about 130 years' by 1967, according to its users, James Smith & Son (Redditch) – established 1698. The Willimantic and Merrick thread boxes are American, probably late nineteenth century

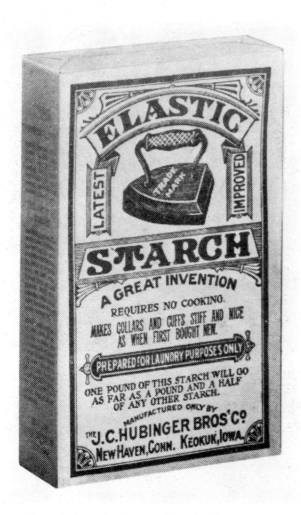

122 Kellogg cornflakes carton, *c.* 1910. 'The sweetheart of the corn' is on the left-hand side panel: this drawing, bought by Will Kellogg from a printing firm called the Ketterlinus Lithographing Co of Philadelphia, was a feature of Kellogg packaging and advertising for many years

121 Carton for Elastic starch. The flatiron trade mark was widely seen in the United States in the early 1880s . . . and long afterwards

123 The first sealed carton for butter, introduced (and nationally advertised) in 1901; printed in brown and red on yellow. The wording on the end read 'Creation's Cleanest Creamery'

124 Quaker Oats *c.* 1908. An English version of the Quaker is seen in a poster of ten years earlier, in plate 207

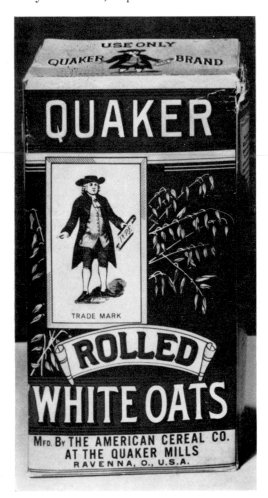

125 The Uneeda carton (page 68) in a stack of biscuit cartons – an advertisement illustration from the early 1920s. Though the package designs had probably been changed, some of the brands are of earlier date than Uneeda – Social Tea Biscuits, 1886; Fig Newtons, 1892; Graham Crackers, 1898. Uneeda were introduced in 1899, Nabisco (sugar wafers) in 1901, Zu Zu also in 1901, Baronet in 1908, Lemon Snaps in 1921 . . . all by the National Biscuit Company, New York

126 The earliest known metal box used in commercial packaging: a lead canister with engraved paper label in which Fribourg & Treyer sold snuff in the 1780s

127 Two-pound can of carrots and gravy by John Gamble & Co (successors to Donkin & Hall and Donkin, Hall & Gamble), London, 1824. The embossed lettering is on a metal strip attached to the can by two dabs of solder (page 72)

[*Other early food cans: plates 156–163*]

128 Box for Royal Patent Congreve matches, probably J. Hynam's, of Finsbury, London, *c.* 1845

130 Late nineteenth-century tin for Day & Martin's blacking – a product mentioned in *Pickwick Papers* (but sold at that time in jars) (page 30)

129 Matchbox for H. J. Oldenburg, whose match factory established at Björneborg, Finland, in 1856 became one of the most important in Europe

131 A later example, from New York. 'Concrete' was perhaps not the happiest choice of name for a face powder

## ROYAL PORTRAITS ON TINS

132 As a New Year gift for 1900, Queen Victoria sent a half-pound tin of chocolate to every British soldier fighting in the war in South Africa. An embossed portrait of the Queen formed the centrepiece of the design, and her handwriting was reproduced in facsimile. Most of the boxes were made by Hudson Scott and Sons Ltd, Carlisle. The dies were subsequently destroyed so that the design could not be commercialized

133 Six-sided metal box for Barringer & Brown's Prize Medal Mustard. The borders and wording were transfer-printed in black and gold-lacquered, but the three main pictures were lithographed prints on paper, stuck on the front panels. They showed Prince Edward and Princess Alexandra, and, between them, a bouquet. At the base is the wording 'Flowers Patent. Tin Plate Decorating Co. Neath'. Late 1870s

134 Biscuit tin transfer-printed by Ben. George, Patentee, London (page 73). Its design recalls the conventional-ized arabesques of Owen Jones, and may have been his work: Jones died in 1874 and Huntley & Palmers did not receive the formal warrant of Royal appointment until 1885, but research by T. A. B. Corley, of the Department of Economics at Reading University, has shown that they were Purveyors to the Queen from July 1867 onwards and confirmed that Jones designed labels and exhibition showcases for them

135 Part of a sheet of thin paper transfers (decalcomanias) for metal box decoration – probably for a Player's cigarette tin in the 1890s

136 Tin for Huntley & Palmers' biscuits by Huntley, Boorne & Stevens. *Moiré métallique*, with transfer-printed posy in colour on the lid, *c.* 1880

137 Another early tin by Huntley, Boorne & Stevens, in monochrome; one of the few reflections in package design of the Artistic Printing movement of the 1870s and 1880s. [Plate 169 shows the back of this tin]

138 Peek, Frean & Co, established in 1857, made a great feature of their 'enamelled', *i.e.* tin-printed, biscuit tins in this 1887 export price list (printed by Riddle & Couchman, lithographers, London). The Patent Air-tight Soldered Tin was available in ½, 1, 2 and 9 lb sizes; it had won a silver medal at the International Health Exhibition, London, 1884

140 The *Through the Looking Glass* biscuit tin of 1892, by Barringer, Wallis & Manners of Mansfield (page 94)

139 Nursery-rhyme tin, intended for re-use as a tea-caddy. It bears the imprint BRYANT & MAY, PATENTEES, LONDON, and was made by Huntley, Boorne and Stevens *c.* 1880. An early example of tin-printing, in black, gold-lacquered. (The lid is not original)

## LITERARY TASTES

141 Biscuit tin for Huntley & Palmers, probably by Huntley, Boorne & Stevens *c.* 1903 or earlier. From these Reading firms, one of the book titles, *History of Reading*, is nicely ambiguous. The idea of making containers to look like books is very old: the British Museum has a portable bookcase or travelling library of 1619–25 in the shape of a folio volume, with shelf-space inside to hold 44 (real) books

142 Tin by Barringer and Co for Queen Victoria's golden jubilee, 1887. The transfer-printed pictures include coronation ceremony, royal residences, and three Prime Ministers. Width 8⅝ in.

143 When the *Mauretania* was the newest Atlantic liner, views of the ship appeared on this tin by Huntley, Boorne & Stevens for Huntley & Palmers (page 94)

## ORNAMENTAL METAL BOXES

Fancy tins such as these found a place as ornaments on cottage mantlepieces and kitchen dressers long after their original contents had been used; they were 're-use containers' before the phrase was coined

144 Tin (for tea?) by Barringer Wallis & Manners, 1906, with printed decoration said to be based on traditional Eastern porcelain design. Width 5 in.

145 Huntley & Palmers' Christmas biscuit tin for 1909 – a 'Sèvres casket' by Huntley, Boorne & Stevens, with roll-top lid. The colour scheme was predominantly green, rose-red and gold, with full-colour pictures. The same shape had been used with a different surface design in 1906

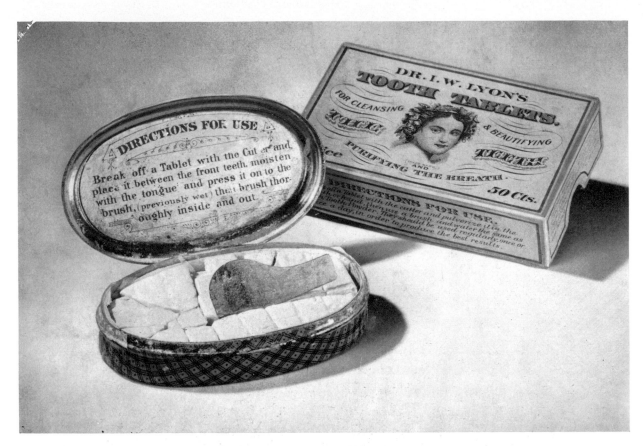

146 Perhaps the earliest American example of the decorated metal box; a flat oval tin for Dr I. W. Lyon's Tooth Tablets, introduced in 1866 (page 77). The tin was sold in the cardboard box seen on its right. The portrait of Dr Lyon's wife, used as a trademark, was retained in simplified form by his successors in business for many years

AMERICAN
METAL BOXES

147 Tin for Dr Johnson's Educator Crackers

148 Cough-drop tin printed in black and orange by Somers Brothers (page 78). The imprint – noticeably smaller than TRY MOSES' – reads SOMERS BRO'S BROOKLYN N.Y. PAT. APL. 29 1879 JULY 1st 1884

149 Large metal boxes for Parke, Davis's Botanic Drugs

TINS FOR AMERICA'S
DRUGGISTS

150 Tooth-powder tin of 1905 for Dr Graves.
The form of the cap suggests that he followed the
example of Dr Lyon, who had introduced a dis-
pensing cap – which he called a 'telescopic
measuring tube' – in 1891

151

153

152

151 The Gerhard Mennen Chemical Co's original toilet-powder pack of 1892 (page 79). The lid, right, fitted over a sprinkler top.
152 A later version (illustrated here from a giant 'dummy' produced for display purposes). In 1909 a flattened oval shape, 153, replaced the round drums. All by Somers Bros, Brooklyn

154a

154 This round metal box for the Bee clock, made by the Ansonia Clock Co *c.* 1900, had an appropriately 'busy' design. The base was fully occupied by a picture of the manufacturers' works at Brooklyn, 154a. Printed in black on red

155 Souvenir of an otherwise forgotten nineteenth-century designer – wooden dummy, with applied paper decoration, for a Huntley & Palmers' biscuit tin

156 Though the sequence of operations is not entirely clear, this engraving by Navellier shows a French canning factory of the period when food canners were their own can manufacturers, *c.* 1860

156a Nicolas Appert (1749–1841), father of an industry. He took out the world's first canning patent in France in 1810; his name has persisted to the present day in the firm Chevallier-Appert, of Charenton, Paris, now concerned with *produits œnologiques* – for the wine trade rather than solid food preservation

157 Can for four pounds of 'roasted veal' packed by John Gamble & Co for Parry's voyage of 1824 in search of the North-west Passage. The directions on the paper label begin: 'Cut round on the top near to the outer edge with a chisel and hammer'

158 Perhaps the earliest pictorial can-label in existence: used by Reckhow & Larne of Cedar Street, New York. Mid-nineteenth century (?). Found in a house at Salem, Indiana. (Page 77)

159 Soup can with type-set label for Crosse & Blackwell, *c.* 1870. A badge of Royal appointment is obscured by the torn paper in this illustration

160 Label for Libby, McNeill & Libby's corned beef between 1868 and 1875. At this time America had no tin-plate industry of her own; the growth of American canning helped to raise imports of Welsh tinplate from about 4,000 tons to 110,000 tons between 1865 and 1880

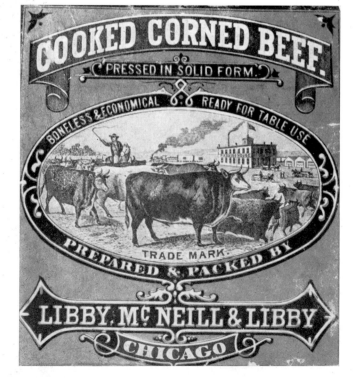

161 Can of consommé soup packed for Schley's Arctic expedition, 1884. Each can was given two coats of red lead and stencilled in white lead with an indication of its contents. Libby, McNeill & Libby, Chicago

EMERGENCY RATION.
(FIELD SERVICE.)

This ration is not to be opened except by order of an Officer, or in extremity.

It is to be carried in the haversack and produced at inspections, &c.

The ration is calculated to maintain strength for 36 hours if eaten in small quantities at a time.

To open the package tear off the band in the centre, when two tins will be found—one containing 4-ozs. Concentrated Beef, and the other 5 ozs. of Cocoa Paste.

Instructions for use are on the lids of the tins.

162 'Twin pack' of 1899 – two cans joined by a metal band soldered to them. One contained 4 oz of concentrated beef, the other 5 oz of cocoa paste. Issued to troops in the Boer War; probably made by John Feaver Ltd, Tower Bridge Road, London (according to the *Tin-Printer & Boxmaker*, October 1958)

163 Food cans and a matchbox left by Scott's Antarctic expedition of 1911. The names of Heinz, Ideal and Plasmon are familiar: the bemedalled label at top left was for a can of pemmican by J. P. Beauvais of Copenhagen

164 Bladders such as this were still employed as containers for artists' colours when the first metal tubes came into use (page 83)

165 The first American shaving cream tube, introduced in 1912 by William Mennen

166 Tobacco paper with wording on balloons as in the modern comic strip. London, late eighteenth century

167 For tobacco again – in America about 100 years later. The shaped metal box for Sensation cut plug, 'more popular every day', was presumably intended to have a re-use value for anglers or handymen

168 Punning picture, Latin motto, revenue stamp *and* embrocation: all for 1s 1½d a bottle in 1909

169 [Back of tobacco tin shown in plate 137]. Long after it had become impossible for a successful manufacturer to sign every one of his packs by hand, facsimile signatures were still talismans to inspire customers' confidence

170

171

Before commerce acquired a style of its own, shop-fronts and package designs were genteel.

Small-paned windows such as those above are echoed in the 'elevation of the principal Establishment' of the London Genuine Tea Company, 23 Ludgate Hill, which was 'printed on the wrapper of every parcel of Tea sold by them and their Agents', 1819

172

By the mid-nineteenth century, cast iron and plate glass were the outward signs of material success – not only in shop-fronts but in the Crystal Palace of 1851 (seen below on a Crosse & Blackwell pot-lid)

173

174a 'MODERN': compare e.g. plates 6, 55, 57, 111

174b SANSERIF: plates 20, 31, 44, 61, 109, 129, 130, 197

174c EGYPTIAN: plates 5, 7, 36, 43, 62, 119, 171

174d TUSCAN: plates 9, 61, 65, 119 (initials), 194

These nineteenth-century letter-forms are usually known by their typographical names, but the illustrations are a reminder that signmakers and package printers were equally concerned with them

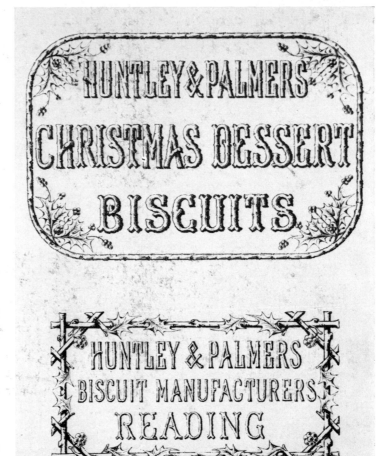

175 Matchbox labels of the 1830s (page 87)

176, 177 Biscuit labels of 1873 – to cover 2 lb tins – and 1875 respectively (page 89)

178

Medals and strapwork link these package designs with traditional farm-implement and machinery decoration

179

178 Printed tin by Huntley, Boorne & Stevens, *c.* 1902–10

179 Tripe can for Libbys, *c.* 1880 – with label in black, red, yellow and blue by Hinds, Ketcham & Co, New York: in 1887, this specialist label-printing firm had addresses in Chicago and Pittsburgh as well as on Broadway

180

180 Cigar-box label, chromo-lithographed and embossed – see also colour plate A

181

181 Manufacturer's transfer on the boiler of a steam-roller: in use in 1925 but designed some years before that date

182 Round box for face powder – similar in style to a rival product, 186 (page 92)

183 The sinuous line again, in a Plasmon package design. Carton by Cropper & Co, *c.* 1907

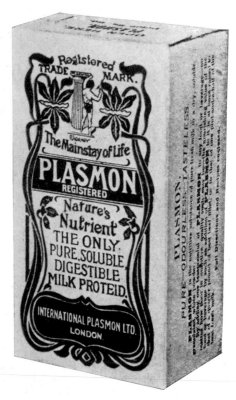

184 Modified *art nouveau* – and a style of brand-name lettering which too many manufacturers were to favour in the next thirty years (e.g. plate 203): the original wrapper for Bournville bars, 1910

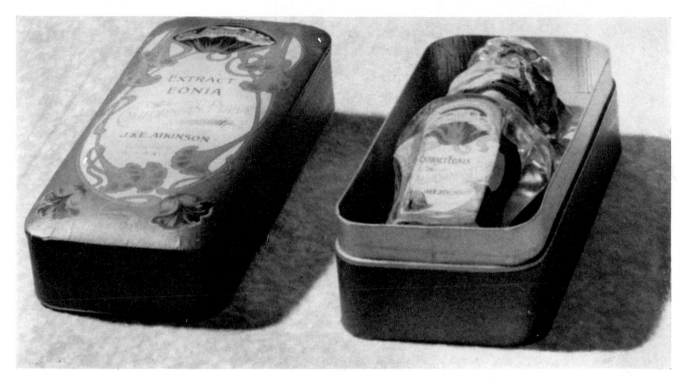

185

186

Family resemblance in packaging. The bottle label and various boxes for Atkinson's Californian Poppy, *c.* 1900, bore similar designs, and the colours of all the items were green, red, yellow and gold. The scent bottle, 185, fitted into a shaped cardboard platform in its protective box (which was lined with gold paper). The square box in 186 held powder in a paper liner with a small gold seal

187 Sir Walter Raleigh, who introduced tobacco from Virginia to England, on a London tobacco paper. Early eighteenth century

188 Dixie Queen on a miniature sack for Civil War soldiers' tobacco, c. 1860–4

189 Pre-Raphaelite beauty on a vase-shaped biscuit tin for Macfarlane Lang & Co, c. 1900. (Made and printed by Barringer, Wallis & Manners – the lid now missing. Described in trade jargon as: Body formed from tapered blank. Lower portion and bottom one piece, solid drawn, the two parts trapped together. Handles tabbed on.) Width across handles $6\frac{1}{4}$ in.

190 Label, current in 1789, showing Anstie's Whistley Mill: the word SNUFF can be seen on the sack in the picture. There is still a Snuff Street in Devizes, but the mill was demolished in 1956 and Ansties' production ceased in the 1960s

191 Chemist's shop of the 1860s (page 93)

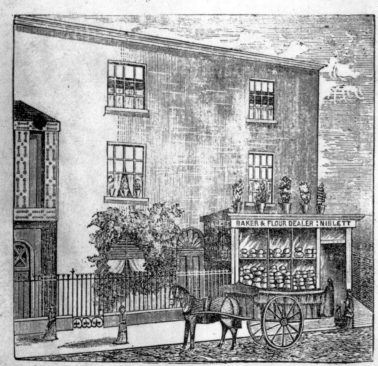

192 Baker's shop of the 1870s – on the baker's own flour bag. In the address, '1 & 2' is on a patch: necessitated by a street renumbering scheme or a printer's error?

193

These illustrate the growth of Huntley & Palmers' Reading, Berks, factory from the 1840s (193; page 72); after 1867 (194); in 1876 (195) . . . and in the early 1950s (196), in a package which still owed much of its character to its Victorian forerunners

194

196

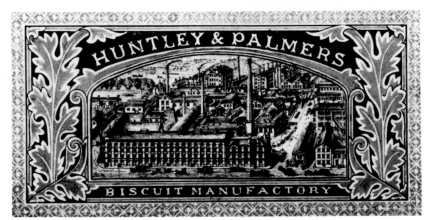

195

The log cabin *motif* in American packaging: 197, a quart bottle for S. T. Drake Plantation Bitters, 1860 – the wording moulded in the glass; 198, a can advertised in 1905. The advertisement, by the J. Walter Thompson Co, referred to Log Cabin Maple Syrup as having been on the market 'now over 20 years'

198

197

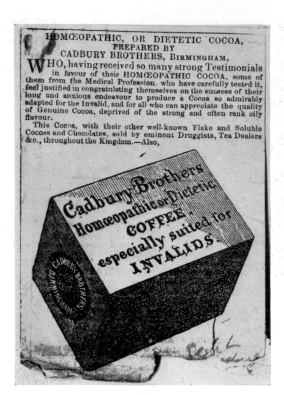

199 The first known advertisement with an illustration of the advertiser's package, *c.* 1849

200 Almanack for 1872 illustrating bottles for four of Rose & Co's Lime-juice Beverages

201 The package at the centre of this showcard was based on a drawing by Fred Walker, R.A. (1840–75) (page 95)

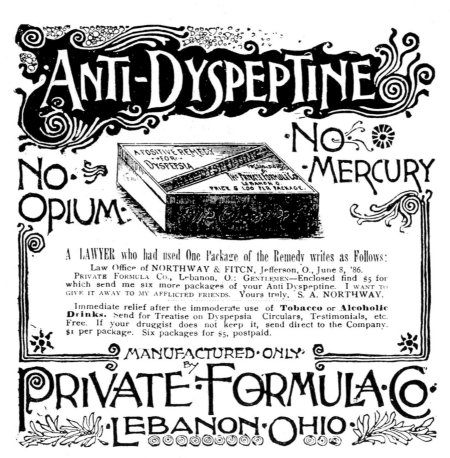

202 A dull package design in a lively advertisement design of 1887 – foreshadowing *art nouveau*

"MY FAVOURITE"

203 From the end of a halcyon age – Rowntree's showcard *c.* 1914 illustrating the Elect Chocolate package

204 George Barham, founder of the Express Dairy Co Ltd, was the first milk bottler in Britain, in 1884. Background to the bottle in the advertising card below is a view of the Express Dairy's premises in North London, opened early in the same decade

(The invention of a milk bottle is credited to Dr Harvey D. Thatcher of Pottsdam, New York, also in the 1880s)

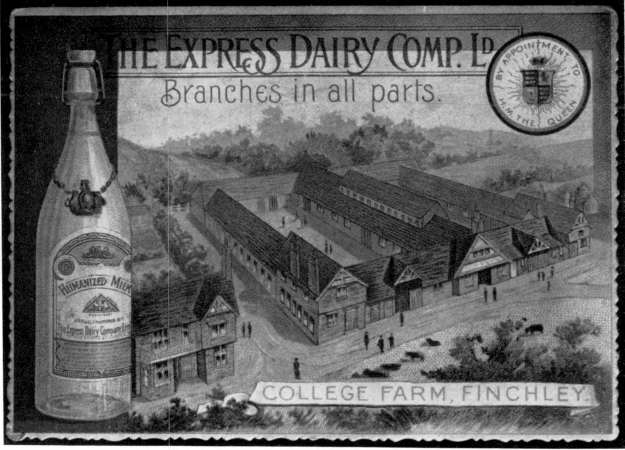

205 Wrappers for Peter's milk chocolate: left, advertised in 1905; right, current sixty years later

206 Page from a catalogue of Jacob & Co, Dublin, c. 1911. The King's Own biscuit tin with its portrait of King George V, who came to the throne in 1910, must have been a novelty at the time. All the tins illustrated were paper-labelled

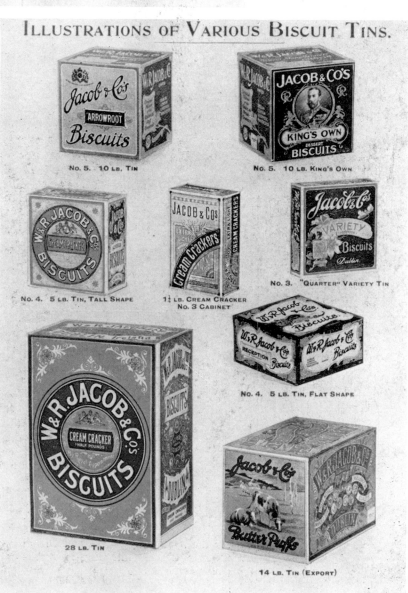

ILLUSTRATIONS OF VARIOUS BISCUIT TINS.

Jacob & Co's
ARROWROOT
Biscuits

No. 5. 10 LB. TIN

JACOB & CO'S
KING'S OWN
DESSERT
BISCUITS

No. 5. 10 LB. KING'S OWN

W.& R. JACOB & Co's
CREAM CRACKER
BISCUITS

No. 4. 5 LB. TIN, TALL SHAPE

JACOB & CO'S
Cream Crackers
EXTRA LIGHT

1½ LB. CREAM CRACKER
No. 3 CABINET

Jacob & Co's
VARIETY
Biscuits
Dublin

No. 3. "QUARTER" VARIETY TIN

W.& R. Jacob & Co's
Biscuits
RECEPTION
Biscuits

No. 4. 5 LB. TIN, FLAT SHAPE

W.R. JACOB & Co's
CREAM CRACKER
HALF POUNDS
BISCUITS

28 LB. TIN

Jacob & Co's
Butter Puffs

14 LB. TIN (EXPORT)

207 Packaged branded goods predominate among the products advertised on this hoarding in Bolton, Lancashire, *c.* 1898 – Bovril, Gilbey's wines and spirits, Colman's starch and Zebra grate polish among them, as well as several products mentioned in earlier pages of this book

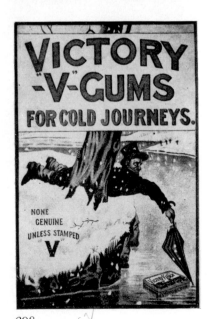

The design of the Victory V-Cough Gums poster, top right, was modified for the showcard, 208; a detail from this, illustrating the tin, is reproduced on right

208

208a